1986

W

Contents

Page

Universities, Polytechnics and other Colleges of
Higher Education................................... 5
English Language Schools...................... 31
Business Schools and Secretarial Colleges.......... 51
Independent Colleges of Further Education and
Tutorial Colleges............................... 59
Independent Boarding Schools................... 91
Reply coupons.............................. 137,140
Index....................................... 138

Foreword by Sir Peter Tennant, some time fellow of Queens' College, Cambridge, member of the Diplomatic Service and former Director General of the British National Export Council.

"Educ: during the holidays from Eton". So runs Osbert Sitwell's entry in Who's Who. This facetious comment sums up an aspect of education which is of great importance to British people. The best educational heritage of this country is to be found in the life of its people at work and play, in their buildings and countryside, in their arts and music and writing.

The educational scene in Britain presents a pattern of the greatest diversity. Visitors from other countries come to Britain more and more to enjoy the variety of choice available in our universities, colleges, adult education establishments and schools.

Higher education covers every known discipline, and perhaps for foreigners the most important ones have been medicine, the sciences, engineering, economics and law. Leading citizens in many countries of the world have benefited from the experience of higher and secondary education in this country. The English language as a lingua franca is in itself an essential tool of international life nowadays, whether in business, the professions or public service and in the last 50 years there has been an explosive growth in English language schools.

The value of British education to untold numbers of individuals in other countries is demonstrated in the first instance by those who were brought up in childhood by British nannies, governesses and tutors, often leading to education in a British boarding school and later at university. These rather selective groups of people have been followed by many thousands from all over the world who come to our country to learn the language and acquire academic degrees or professional qualifications to further their careers.

The heritage of education in Britain is not a static structure but a moving and growing one. Renewal and innovation have been its hallmarks. This heritage offers an unrivalled access to knowledge and opinions on all aspects of life past and present, while students are left to make up their own minds on all these problems with the help of the inherited wisdom of a country which has learned much from a long history. We invite our foreign friends to join with us in enjoying this heritage.

2

Universities, Polytechnics and other Colleges of Higher Education

6

UNIVERSITY COLLEGE OF WALES ABERYSTWYTH

The campus at Aberystwyth has been known as The University College of Wales since its establishment in 1872. The founders could not have even dreamed that by 1984 the College would have 3000 students and be the oldest of seven institutions which now comprise the federal University of Wales and which is the second largest university in Britain. Five hundred of the College's students are graduates studying for higher degrees and almost 200 are from overseas representing over 50 counties. Aberystwyth town received its Royal Charter in 1277 but there had been a renowned monastery nearby in the sixth century and on the hill above the town the remains of a large Celtic fort remain visible after 2500 years.

Most of the College is now housed in modern buildings on the fine 400-acre campus overlooking the sea. Student housing is mostly on-campus and provides over 2000 beds. Students from overseas are placed in single study-bedrooms and have a choice of prepared meals or cooking their own food. A number of furnished flats are available for students accompanied by families. The College library has over 350,000 books and adjacent to the campus is the National Library of Wales with immense resources deriving from its legal right to a free copy of every publication in Britian.

The College has Faculties of Arts, Science, Economic & Social Studies, Law, Music and Education. It is also closely linked with the College of Librarianship and the Welsh Plant Breeding Station. The Faculty of Science has Schools of Mathematics, Agricultural Sciences, and Biological Sciences, and departments of Chemistry, Geography, Geology and Physics. All teaching departments provide tuition for the Bachelor, Master and PhD degrees of the University of Wales. Full details of undergraduate courses are published in the 'Prospectus' available free of charge from the Registrar. Enquiries about tuition and research facilities for graduate students should mention the proposed subject of study.

We shall be holding an Open Day on 29th September, but visitors are welcome at any other time by appointment.

The University of Wales at Aberystwyth,
Old College,
King Street,
Aberystwyth, SY23 2AX.
Tel: 0970 3177.

UNIVERSITY OF BATH

Formerly a College of Advanced Technology, the institution received its Royal Charter as Bath University of Technology in 1966 and changed its name to the University of Bath in 1971. Particularly strong in engineering, science and management subjects, it provides courses designed to produce graduates who are able to take up positions of responsibility in industry, commerce and government. Situated on a hill overlooking the beautiful City of Bath, one of Europe's most fascinating cities, famous for its Roman remains and Georgian architecture.

Undergraduate Courses

Details of the various undergraduate courses available at Bath are listed below:
European Studies, Applied Biology, Applied Physics, Architectural Studies, Biochemistry, Building Engineering, Business Administration, Chemistry, Chemical Engineering, Economics, Economics and Politics, Economics with Computing and Statistics, Electrical and Electronic Engineering, Engineering (including Aeronautical, Mechanical, Systems, and Thermal Power), Engineering with French, Engineering with German, Horticulture, Manufacturing, Materials Science, Mathematics, Mathematical Studies, Mathematics and Computing, Pharmacology, Physics, Physics with Geophysics, Physics with Physical Electronics, Social Sciences, Sociology, Statistics, Architecture, Pharmacy.

Postgraduate Opportunities

Excellent research facilities exist in the following Schools of the University, where students are registered for a PhD or Masters Degree by research:
Architecture and Building Engineering, Biological Sciences, Chemical Engineering, Chemistry, Education, Electrical Engineering, Engineering, Humanities and Social Sciences, Management, Materials Sciences, Mathematics, Modern Languages, Pharmacy and Pharmacology, Physics.

Full time courses leading to a Masters Degree are available in:
Applied Social Studies, Business Administration, Crop Production, Development Studies, Education, Fiscal Studies, Fluid Power Technology, Fluid Power Systems and Design, Industrial Relations, Internal Combustion Engineering, Public Policy, Social Analysis of Science & Technology, Translation and Linguistics (for Arabic speakers).

For further information and prospectuses please get in touch with Mr George O'Brien, Senior Assistant Registrar, University of Bath, Bath BA2 7AY, England, if possible indicating the specific area you are interested in.

BRUNEL UNIVERSITY

Brunel University is unusual in that it is named after a person and not a place. Isambard Kingdom Brunel was a pioneer and innovator in nineteenth century Britain in engineering, and his great engineering works (in particular, bridges) still stand today as testimony to his imagination.

The University received its charter in 1966 as a technological university; it had been previously a College of Advanced Technology. As a technological university Brunel provides courses which are academic in the traditional sense but which are also in tune with the contemporary interests and concerns of industry, commerce, and state services such as the Education and Health Services. It has forged links with local industry, and its location is an important aspect of its success in this respect.

The University is unique in that *all* its undergraduate courses (4 years in length) include "sandwich" industrial training. Employers clearly value this extra dimension, judging by the high rate of unemployment of Brunel Graduates.

In the field of research Brunel has a reputation for vigour and carries out important work in the fields of Technology, Social Sciences, Mathematics and Statistics, and Education.

Location
Brunel is situated on the western edge of London within easy reach of the centre of the city, and of Windsor, Eton, the River Thames and the attractive Chiltern Hills. A second campus, housing the Faculty of Education and Design is at Egham in Surrey.

The main campus itself is modern and spacious, and enlivened by the small river Pinn. The Egham campus is based on an impressive Victorian building set in beautiful surroundings overlooking the Thames.

Courses
Brunel offers courses in: Biology, Biochemistry, Chemistry, Mathematics, Computer Science, Physics, Economics, Law, Psychology, Sociology, Government and Politics, Mechanical Engineering, Electrical and Electronic Engineering, Materials and Production technology.

Where the existing undergraduate programme does not meet the needs of any individual (for example where the study of any unusual mixture of subjects is required) it is usually possible to draw up a special programme.

Facilities
Students from abroad are guaranteed accommodation in the University residences. They are each allotted a personal tutor. Their general welfare is also the concern of the Overseas Students Tutor. Not only does the University have the advantage of being near London but it also provides a wide range of cultural and sporting facilities on campus. The Students' Union offers a wide range of clubs and societies, bars, discos and 'live' group concerts.

Visitors are welcome to the Uxbridge campus but it is suggested they telephone beforehand so that directions can be given concerning access.

All Information and Enquiries: The Public Relations Officer, Brunel University, Uxbridge UB8 3PH. Tel: Uxbridge (0895) 37188.

UNIVERSITY OF DURHAM

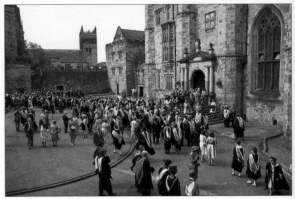

The Courtyard of University College during a degree ceremony.

The City of Durham

The University of Durham is the third oldest university in England after Oxford and Cambridge. Durham (pop. 25,000) is dominated by a 12th century castle, now a university residence, a cathedral and many older buildings which are now part of the University.

Durham is in the N.E. of England, three hours from London by train. Edinburgh, the capital of Scotland, is a two-hour journey north. Newcastle upon Tyne (pop. 1m.) with an airport, seaport, theatres and modern shopping centres, is 15 miles away.

The University

The previous Chancellor of the University was Malcolm MacDonald and he was succeeded by Dame Margot Fonteyn de Arias. The Vice-Chancellor is Professor Holliday, a marine biologist, who is also a member of many government committees and a Director of Shell U.K. Limited. The status of Durham within the university system is reflected by such leaders of national eminence.

Students

There are 4,600 students in the University, including 600 postgraduates. There are students from 51 different countries with the largest groups coming from the U.S.A., Germany and Saudi Arabia.

Entry standards are amongst the highest in Britain. Durham is a caring community with 80% of students living in college accommodation. 95% successfully complete their courses and then achieve success in employment and subsequent careers.

The Academic Departments

The Faculty of Science represents the departments of Applied Physics and Electronics, Botany, Chemistry, Engineering, Geology, Mathematics, Physics and Zoology. In the Social Science Faculty there are departments of Anthropology, Archaeology, Economic History, Economics (with subsidiary courses in Accountancy), Geography, Law, Politics, Psychology and Sociology.

The Departments of Classics, English, French, German, History, Italian, Music, Oriental Studies, Philosophy, Russian, Spanish and Theology are grouped in the Faculty of Arts. In addition, there is a large School of Education.

A popular course for overseas students is the Master's Degree in Applied Linguistics with special reference to the teaching of English as a foreign language.

The University has a Centre for Middle Eastern and Islamic Studies and there are also close links with China. An International Festival of Oriental Music, under the patronage of Princess Alexandra, is held in Durham in association with the world famous Museum of Oriental Art.

University of Durham,
Old Shire Hall,
Durham DH1 3HP.
Tel: 0385 64466.

UNIVERSITY OF ESSEX

Essex is one of Britain's newer and smaller universities. Founded in 1964, it has some 3,100 students, some 650 of whom are studying for post-graduate qualifications. The modern buildings of the University are set in 200 acres of eighteenth century parkland, just two miles from the centre of Colchester, a busy market town of 140,000 inhabitants.

Colchester is 54 miles (87 km) from London. Trains are frequent and take less than an hour. Easy access to the galleries, museums, theatres and sights of London has both academic and social advantages.

The University's policy has been to concentrate its academic resources on a relatively small number of large departments, thus enabling each department to include specialists in a whole range of subjects. Its 15 Departments — Art History and Theory, Biology, Chemistry, Computer Science, Economics, Electrical Engineering Science, Government, History, Language and Linguistics, Law, Literature, Mathematics, Philosophy, Physics and Sociology — offer:

(a) Bachelor degree schemes (BA. B.Sc or LL.B) normally of three years in duration
(b) Masters degree schemes — either taught courses lasting one year or in Biology, Chemistry, Computer Science, Electrical Engineering Science, Mathematics and Physics one year's full-time investigational research
(c) Post-graduate Diploma courses of nine months or a year
(d) Certificate courses of one term or nine months
(e) Research degrees of M. Phil and Ph.D, involving two and three years minimum full-time research at Essex.

Essex welcomes students who wish to spend a term or a year at the University on a non-graduating basis. Arrangements can be made with your University for your undergraduate studies at Essex to be counted towards your degree.

Studying at Essex is relatively inexpensive. Most accommodation is conveniently located so little time or money is spent on daily travel. For their first year at Essex, all unmarried students from overseas are guaranteed a single place in University-owned accommodation. Each student had his own study-bedroom and shares the bathroom and kitchen with other residents of the flat.

We will be happy to provide you with further information, if you write indicating your interests, to:

The Admissions Officer,
University of Essex,
Wivenhoe Park,
Colchester, Essex CO4 3SQ.

11

HERIOT-WATT UNIVERSITY, EDINBURGH

Heriot-Watt University received its Royal Charter as a University in 1966, but its origins are traced back through a century and a half of achievement in technical education and active cooperation with industry in training and research in direct line from the Edinburgh School of Arts, founded in 1821. It takes its name from two famous Scots: George Heriot (goldsmith to King James VI and I) who left his considerable fortune to fund education in his native Edinburgh, and James Watt, engineer and pioneer of steam power.

It is a technological university on the move. It is moving from Edinburgh's historic centre to a new 250 acre parkland campus within the city at Riccarton — a popular location for conferences and which in vacation periods provides residential accommodation to visitors to Scotland's capital. It is also on the move to innovate, to enhance an already considerable reputation for its teaching and research in science and engineering, and to develop areas of study of direct industrial, commercial and social relevance.

With just over 3,000 students it is small enough to respond quickly to change. It was the first British university to establish a 'Research Park' where companies in the forefront of high technology work in close liaison with the University. It is one of the two British universities designated as a 'centre of excellence' in advanced studies relating to petroleum engineering, and a leading centre for research in marine technology. Its research successes range from biotechnology and microelectronics to acoustics and computer-aided engineering, but it is on its degree courses that its solid foundation is built.

Engineering and science are complemented by courses in business and management, in accountancy and training for the actuarial profession. An important new postgraduate course is in international banking and finance. Degree courses in architecture and town planning are supplemented by postgraduates studies in urban design and conservation.

Heriot-Watt has long enjoyed a tradition of welcoming students from overseas. Its facilities for sport are among the best in Britain and its medical and other caring services for its students match the excellence of its academic reputation. Its location, in Scotland's beautiful capital city with its lively social and cultural life, adds to its attraction.

Its four faculties offer the following first degree courses: **Science** — biochemistry, brewing, marine biology, microbiology, chemistry, computer science, mathematics, actuarial mathematics and statistics, pharmacy, physics. **Engineering** — building, building economics and quantity surveying, estate management, chemical engineering, civil engineering, electrical and electronic engineering, mechanical engineering, offshore engineering. **Economic and Social Studies** — accountancy and computer science, accountancy and finance, business organisation, economics, languages (interpreting and translating). **Environmental Studies** — architecture, landscape architecture, town planning. All departments have facilities for postgraduate study and research and a range of diploma and Master's degree courses are offered.

For information on admission to undergraduate or postgraduate courses, or on vacation residential facilities, write to: The Secretary, Heriot-Watt University, Edinburgh EH1 1HX.

IMPERIAL COLLEGE OF SCIENCE AND TECHNOLOGY

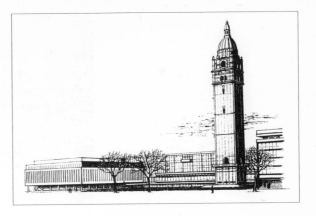

Imperial College, one of the Colleges in the University of London, was founded in 1907, in the words of the Charter, 'to give the highest specialized instruction and to provide the fullest equipment for the most advanced training and research'.

An undergraduate degree course here provides young people with the best possible base for a career in a very wide range of science and engineering fields, plus a valuable preparation for their future in general. At postgraduate level degrees offered are by coursework of one year's duration, or by research leading to a doctorate. The College has close connections with industry, professional bodies and government and the resulting flow of knowledge is particularly useful to students taking one of the many one year full-time postgraduate courses, or carrying out research.

There is a modern sports centre on campus, which includes a heated swimming pool, and facilities are available through the College for almost any sport. Every registered student is a member of the Students' Union and for those who wish to be involved in athletic, social and recreational activities the Union provides an endless variety from the very silliest to the most sober.

The College is situated close to the centre of London so that all the amenities of a large cosmopolitan capital are within a few minutes travelling time. It is in the fortunate position of being able to offer all overseas first-year undergraduates a place in College residential accommodation; and, apart from students already living in London, can offer places in College halls and houses for all other first-year undergraduates. High priority is given to overseas postgraduates in allocating residence places and the Student Services Office assists should any accommodation problems arise.

For further information about undergraduate or postgraduate courses at the College write to:

The Registrar,
Imperial College of Science and Technology,
London SW7 2AZ.

UNIVERSITY OF KEELE

The University of Keele is set in beautiful English Countryside, close to the ancient town of Newcastle-under-Lyme and the Staffordshire Potteries. The medieval cities of Chester and Shrewsbury, the picturesque areas of the Peak District, the Welsh mountains, the Lake District and Stratford-on-Avon are all readily accessible. Keele is one of a handful of 'new' British universities founded since 1950 — the first such in fact. Keele's basic undergraduate course was conceived to provide 'the right balance between specialization and expert knowledge on the one hand and a wide outlook and general understanding on the other.'

Keele offers a wide range of 3 and 4 year degree courses for overseas students. Most students follow dual honours courses and it is possible to combine unusual as well as traditional subjects. Honours subjects may be chosen from any two of the following:

American Studies, Applied Social Studies, Applied Statistics and Operational Research, * Biochemistry, * Biology, * Chemistry, Classics, * Computer Science, Economics, * Electronics, English, French, Geography, * Geology, German, Greek Studies, History, Integrated Physical Sciences, International Relations, Law, Management Science, * Mathematics, Music, philosophy, P.P.E. (Philosophy, Politics and Economics studied as an integrated degree course), * Physics, Politics, Psychology, Russian Studies, Sociology and Social Anthropology.

* Students who follow honours courses in two natural sciences may take single honours in their final year.

Junior Year Abroad: American students normally attend the University for one year or one semester and can take courses in the subjects of their choice. Full credit is assured if the students own college or university arranges the transfer to Keele.

Accommodation on campus, in modern single-study bedrooms, is guaranteed to all overseas students.

Applicants and their families are invited to visit the University on the afternoon of Saturday 13th October 1984, but it is possible to look around the campus at any time and individual arrangements may be made through the Senior Tutor's Office, University of Keele, Keele, Staffordshire ST5 5BG.

UNIVERSITY OF KENT AT CANTERBURY

A view of the city of Canterbury from the campus of the University of Kent at Canterbury.

A Tradition of Scholarship

The University of Kent at Canterbury, one of Great Britain's modern universities, is situated on a hillside in the most ancient and beautiful of English Cathedral cities, a city which boasts a tradition of learning and scholarship that stretches back over a millennium.

Collegiate System

One of its most distinctive features is its collegiate system. Kent is organised into Colleges as are the ancient universities of Oxford and Cambridge. By bringing together teaching and research, residence and catering under one roof in modern well-endowed buildings on a 300 acre campus, the University has revived and invigorated a well-respected tradition in English university education.

Academic Structure

Kent has a flexible and imaginative academic structure. Students are admitted to one of the three Faculties of Humanities, Natural Sciences and Social Sciences or the School of Mathematical Studies. The lack of a rigid departmental structure has enabled the promotion of interdisciplinary approaches to study in the 200 degree programmes available.

Centre of Excellence

The University has acquired distinction as a centre of excellence in teaching and research in many areas, including: **Natural Sciences**, especially in such areas as Biotechnology, Digital or Molecular Electronics, Computer Science, Optical Fibre technology and Chemical Physics; the **Social Sciences**, including Accounting, Economics and Law; in **Mathematical Studies**, including Actuarial Science and Statistics, and in the **Humanities**, including English, History and European Studies.

Academic and Social Facilities

There is a large and spacious library with over half a million books and periodicals and extensive computing facilities based on a local area network.

The social and cultural facilities on the campus are excellent, with a superbly equipped sports centre and over 60 acres of playing fields. The Gulbenkian Theatre, which is the major centre for drama in the region, the Regional Film Theatre and a wide programme of musical events and exhibitions enrich the university's cultural life..

Accommodation

Students from overseas are guaranteed accommodation in one of the Colleges or in self-catering residences on campus for at least one year provided they firmly accept a firm offer of admission by 31 August and have completed and fulfilled all conditions of entry.

Further Information

For further information please contact: Mrs. Lee Marshall, MA, Senior Assistant Registrar for Admissions, The Registry, University of Kent, Canterbury, Kent CT2 7NZ. Tel: 0227 66822. Telex: 965449.

UNIVERSITY OF LANCASTER

One of Britain's Modern Universities

The University of Lancaster is situated in a beautiful part of North-West England. It is one of the largest of Britain's new universities, founded in the 1960s, and provides excellent facilities for undergraduate and postgraduate study and research. Lancaster offers a wide range of first degree, higher degree and diploma courses in the sciences, business and management studies, social sciences and humanities. Its 4,500 full-time students use specially designed teaching, research and computer facilities, up-to-date laboratories and a well-stocked library.

International Community

The University is a lively international community. This year there are over 500 students from 70 countries studying at Lancaster. Many of the University's 34 departments have an international reputation for teaching and research. Teaching in small groups forms an important part of undergraduate and postgraduate study.

The friendly atmosphere of the eight residential campus colleges brings together students and staff from a wide variety of disciplines and backgrounds.

All overseas students from outside the European Community are offered the opportunity of a study bedroom on campus during their first year. Undergraduates from outside the European Community can live on campus for the duration of their studies.

Living at Lancaster

The University lies within the boundary of the historic city of Lancaster, yet overlooks Morecambe Bay and the mountains of the Lake District. Academic departments, colleges, library, banks, shops and sporting and recreational facilities are all found on campus. Trains from London to Lancaster take three hours. Manchester International Airport is one hour away by car.

Major Centres

The University's School of Management and Organisational Sciences is one of the largest and most experienced in the United Kingdom. The Institute for English Language Education is a major centre providing tuition in English as a foreign language to students from overseas.

Academic Courses

The University has more than 120 first degree schemes offering specialisation in one or more major subjects. Degree courses are flexible and allow for a combination of subjects to be studied together. At postgraduate level a wide range of taught Master's degree courses, which normally last 12 months, and diploma courses are offered. Well established Junior Year Abroad programs provide North American students with an extensive choice of fully accredited courses.

For further information please write to: The Registrar, University House, The University of Lancaster, Lancaster LA1 4YW, United Kingdom. Telephone: Lancaster (STD 0524) 65201.

UNIVERSITY OF LIVERPOOL

The University of Liverpool is one of Britain's great civic universities. It has an international reputation for the quality of its teaching and research and is one of the few British universities to be awarded the Queen's Award for Technological Achievement.

In common with other British universities Liverpool offers undergraduate and postgraduate degrees in arts, education, engineering, law, medicine and dental surgery, science and social science. Unlike most other universities it also offers courses in veterinary science and tropical medicine — the University has one of Britain's six veterinary schools and it validates courses arranged by the world-renowned Liverpool School of Tropical Medicine.

The University welcomes overseas students and in the current year there are students here from 92 different nations. Some courses are specially designed for overseas students, including the Master in Public Administration course, the Diploma in Marine Pollution Chemistry and many of the courses offered by the Liverpool School of Tropical Medicine.

Each of the University's eight Faculties is strongly committed to research — the externally funded research support offered to the University exceeded £6,000,000 in 1982-3. Some research groups span more than one Faculty: these groups include a Centre for Latin American Studies, a Centre for Marine and Coastal Studies, an Institute for Human Ageing and a Marine Transport Centre.

Students at Liverpool have access to a library with more than one million volumes and a computer laboratory with four main-frame computers and a wide range of micro-computers. More than three quarters of the student population use the computing facilities as part of their course.

The University is situated near the centre of Liverpool, a seaport with a tradition of welcoming visitors from overseas. The University's halls of residence provide accommodation of a high standard for three thousand students within easy reach of the facilities of the University and the attractions of the City of Liverpool, and a comfortable, three hour train journey from London.

The University will be open to visitors on Tuesday, 1 May, 1984 when the University will hold its annual Open Day and visitors are also welcome at other times. Individual visitors can make their own arrangements to visit the University at any time of the year by telephoning Alison Elliott, 051-709 6022, extension 2097. Further information about the Open Day or about academic matters can be obtained from:

The Registrar,
University of Liverpool,
P.O. Box 147,
Liverpool L69 3BX.
Telephone 051-709 6022, Telex 627095.

UNIVERSITY OF SALFORD

Situated two miles from the centre of Manchester and ten miles from Manchester International Airport the University offers a wide range of degree courses mainly in SCIENCE and ENGINEERING but also in Business and Administration, Finance and Accounting, Economics, Geography, Sociology, and European Languages.

Salford is a Campus University in the heart of the Greater Manchester conurbation continuing the great British traditions of education, a new University but with roots way back in the 19th Century, growing then out of an industrial and social revolution, thriving now on the challenge of new technology and the changing social order.

Salford offers programmes of study leading to first degrees (BSc, BA) and to higher degrees (MSc, MA, MPhil, PhD), with a number of Diploma and Certificate courses including a Certificate of English as a Foreign Language. A wide variety of courses is available for those seeking a Junior Year Abroad.

For overseas students who do not have the usual academic entry requirements the University's Matriculation Unit has a Preliminary Year with courses in English language and a choice from Mathematics, Physics, Chemistry, and Biology, appropriate to the first degree programme which will follow. A choice of introductory English language courses of different durations and levels is also offered in the Unit.

The University is a busy Conference Centre with modern lecture theatres, good residential accommodation and a high standard of catering. As such its location close to the centre of a network of road, rail and air communication is ideal. By rail we are less than 3 hours from the centre of London. A shuttle air service operates Manchester-London Heathrow. We are only 2 hours by road from the Scottish Border country, the Lake District, the Yorkshire Dales, the Derbyshire Peak District and the North Wales Coast.

The Overseas Educational Development Office is experienced in the provision of educational services and expertise to institutions abroad.

For further information please write giving details of the facilities or courses (please mention subject/s and level) which interest you to the Public Relations Officer:

Room 102GT,
Registrar's Department,
University of Salford,
Salford M5 4WT.
Telex 668680 SULIB).

UNIVERSITY OF SOUTHAMPTON

The city of Southampton lies on the south coast of England, about 75 miles southwest of London. It is Britain's main ocean passenger port. The city has enjoyed recent modern development and, together with Portsmouth to the east, lies in an area of rapidly increasing economic importance. The present population is nearly 210,000. Although very much a commercial and light industrial centre Southampton is a fine clean city with wide streets and many open public places. Great care has been taken that the modern development is in keeping with the historical character of the city. From Paleolithic hunters through the ages to the Romans, the Saxons, the Danes, the Normans and on to the modern times Southampton has been an important settlement. There is easy access to many nearby places of interest from spas and seaside resorts to stately homes and parks. The beautiful unspoiled countryside includes the New Forest, the Hampshire Downs and the Isle of Wight.

The University of Southampton was given its Charter in 1952 but has its origins in the Hartley Institution, a local cultural institute which was founded in 1862. The University now has just over 6,300 full-time students of whom about 1000 are post-graduates and 400 are from overseas.

Undergraduate and postgraduate courses and research facilities are provided in eight Faculties:

Arts
Educational Studies
Engineering and Applied Science
Law

Mathematical Studies
Medicine
Science
Social Sciences.

Except for the Medical and Biological Sciences Building, some ten minutes walk from the main site, and clinical teaching in the local hospitals, all the teaching buildings are on a single site about a mile and a half north from the City centre. The combination of several substantial older buildings and a number of newer ones has been carefully planned to create a sense of spaciousness within the compact but well landscaped campus. Accommodation for just over 2,800 students is provided in a number of Halls of Residence on several sites, within easy reach of the main teaching buildings.

Enquiries, giving the subject of interest, should be addressed to:

The Academic Registrar,
The University,
Highfield,
Southampton SO9 5NH.
Telephone: Southampton (0703) 559122, extension 712/2379.

UNIVERSITY OF STIRLING

Description of Campus

The University of Stirling was established by Royal Charter in 1967 and is the first completely new university in Scotland for over 400 years. Sited on the outskirts of the ancient town of Stirling and within easy access of Edinburgh and Glasgow, the University occupies a magnificent 300 acre estate of mature woodland and park originally constructed for the 18th Century Airthrey Castle. The university is sited on a completely self-contained campus housing an Arts Centre including a Theatre, extensive sports facilities, central library, shopping mall, bank and restaurants. The majority of students are housed in modern campus residences within easy access of all teaching facilities.

Academic Programmes

The University's curriculum covers Arts, Sciences, Social Sciences and Education. The subjects offered are Aquaculture, Accountancy and Business Law, Biochemistry, Biology, Business Studies, Chemistry, Computing Science, Economics, Education, English Studies, Environmental Science, Film and Media Studies, Fine Art, French, German, History, Management Science, Mathematics, Music, Philosophy, Physics, Political Studies, Psychology, Religious Studies, Sociology, Social Anthropology, Social Administration and Spanish. The University offers access to undergraduate courses to 'Study Abroad' students. Graduating students complete BA/BSc at undergraduate level; the research degrees, M.Litt, MSc, PhD at postgraduate level, and a number of taught masters degrees comprising eight months taught coursework and four months research.

Academic Facilities

As a new university, Stirling has developed fresh approaches to university life and education, and from the beginning set out to offer a genuine alternative to the larger urban universities in Scotland. The University operates a semester system (virtually unique in the UK) and has avoided the creation of faculties with rigid subject boundaries. Students normally take three semester units in each of Autumn and Spring semesters. Teaching is conducted through lectures, seminars, tutorials and, for laboratory-based subjects through lab work. The favourable ratio of staff to students means that much of the teaching is conducted in small groups. Grading is done by a continuous assessement system, involving a number of essays or class tests and an examination.

Further Information

Please contact: The Admissions Officer (GT):
University of Stirling,
Stirling FK9 4LA,
Scotland.
Tel: (0786) 3171 Ext. 2268. Telex: 77749.

THE UNIVERSITY OF STRATHCLYDE

In 1964, the Royal College of Science and Technology, with roots going back to 1796, amalgamated with the Scottish College of Commerce to form the University of Strathclyde. The University is situated on its own campus in the centre of the city of Glasgow and has just over 7000 full-time students. Over 5800 are undergraduates while over 1200 study for postgraduate degrees and diplomas. About 900 come from overseas, from over 70 countries.

The University is organised into four Faculties: Science, Engineering, Arts and Social Studies and the Strathclyde Business School. As well as many departments normally found in UK universities, the University includes departments specialising in Applied Physics, Applied Chemistry, Applied Geology, Metallurgy, Biotechnology, Pharmacy, Production Engineering, Marine Technology, Mining and Petroleum Engineering, Librarianship, Administration, Industrial Relations, Marketing, Office Organisation, Hotel Management, Tourism, Bioengineering and Forensic Science (the last three at postgraduate level only).

Undergraduate Study

A wide range of courses is offered with particular emphasis on Applied Science, Applied Social Sciences, Technology (including a wide range of Engineering courses) and Business Studies. As well as students intending to graduate, the University welcomes occasional students intending to study for a year or less.

Postgraduate Study

All departments offer opportunities for research leading to Masters degrees or PhD. There are also many instructional postgraduate courses lasting between nine months and two years for Masters degrees and Postgraduate Diplomas.

Overseas research students are eligible to apply for support from the Overseas Research Student (ORS) Award Scheme.

Access to Higher Education

In conjunction with Glasgow University and Strathclyde Regional Council, the University offers potential overseas students one and two year courses of preparation for university entry.

The University has an extensive range of advisory, welfare and cultural facilities. Most student residences are located on campus close to the Library, Computer Centre and all teaching departments.

For further information, please write to The Academic Registrar, University of Strathclyde, 16 Richmond Street, Glasgow G1 1XQ, Scotland. Telephone No. 041 552 4400. Telex No. Unslib G 77472. Please state clearly the subjects in which you are interested and the level (undergraduate, postgraduate or Access to Higher Education). Prospective students are also welcome to visit the University at any time by prior arrangement with the Academic Registrar or direct with individual departments.

UNIVERSITY OF SURREY

Surrey is a modern university, granted its Royal Charter in 1966. While preserving a strong tradition of engineering from our late 19th century origins in the Battersea Polytechnic Institute, the subjects studied include the biological sciences and music. The philosophy of the University is to pursue both fundamental and applied research and teaching that is relevant to the cultural and practical needs of contemporary society. Technology is one of the most important influences in social change. We see the concept of technology as unifying the scientist, engineer, economist and businessman, all of whose activities will prosper as we strengthen their base in fundamental theoretical knowledge.

The University offers a lively environment for study of a wide range of courses in technology, science and the humanities. The well-equipped modern University buildings lie on a hilltop campus, surrounded by gardens and sports fields. As well as up-to-date lecture theatres, laboratories, computer centre and library, there is attractive campus accommodation available to overseas single students who wish to live there throughout their course of study. There is every facility for sport, entertainment and the arts, both on campus and in Guildford.

Undergraduate Courses

The University offers the following range of Undergraduate Courses leading to the award of a B.Sc. Honours Degree: Chemical Engineering, Mechanical Engineering, Civil Engineering, Engineering (including Industrial Management), Electronic and Electrical Engineering (B.Sc. or MEng.).

Technological Mathematics, Modern Mathematics, Mathematics with Computing Science, Mathematics with Statistics, Mathematics and Economics, Metallurgy & Materials Technology, Physics, Physics with Modern Acoustics, Physics with Microcomputing.

Biochemistry, Biochemistry (Medical), Biochemistry (Toxicology), Chemistry, Nutrition, Nutrition/Food Science, Microbiology, Nursing Studies.

Economics, Economics/Sociology/Statistics, Psychology, Applied Psychology/Sociology, Hotel and Catering Management, Academic and Practical Applications of Music, Music with Applied Physics (Tonmeister), Dance in Society, Linguistics and International Studies (French, German or Russian).

Postgraduate Courses/Research

The University offers a wide range of postgraduate courses in fields allied to those shown above, leading to the award by examination of a Masters Degree, a Postgraduate Diploma, Advanced Diploma or Postgraduate Certificate. MPhil and PhD Higher Degrees by research and thesis are offered in all its Departments. Extensive research facilities, backed up by a powerful Prime computer network, are available to all research students. Departments are always pleased to show visitors the facilities available by appointment.

For further information about the University of Surrey, please contact: The Registrar, University of Surrey, Guildford, Surrey GU2 5XH, U.K.

THE UNIVERSITY OF WARWICK

The University of Warwick was founded in the early 1960s during a period of expansion in higher education. Parliament approved the University's establishment in 1961 and the Royal Charter was received in 1965.

It occupies a 470 acre site given by the City of Coventry and the Warwickshire County Council. Lying two miles outside Coventry, it is centrally situated in the heart of England, and is easily accessible by road, rail and air. Warwickshire contains attractive scenery and nearby towns such as Kenilworth, Warwick and Stratford-upon-Avon are of considerable historical interest.

Academic Information — Postgraduate and undergraduate population totals 5550 (October 1983). Courses/research facilities are offered by the following departments:

Arts — English and Comparative Literary Studies, French, German, History, History of Art, Italian, Centre for the Study of Social History, Theatre Studies, Classics, Film Studies, History of Music, Spanish.

Education — Arts Education, Education, Physical Education, Science Education.

Centre for English Language Teaching.

Science — Biological Sciences, Chemistry and Molecular Sciences, Computer Science, Engineering, Environmental Sciences, Mathematics, Physics, School of Postgraduate Medical Education.

Social Studies — Applied Social Studies, Economics, Industrial and Business Studies, International Studies, Law, Philosophy, Politics, Psychology, Sociology.

The following research centres are based at the University: Centre for Research in Industry, Business and Administration; Industrial Relations Research Unit; Institute for Employment Research; Macroeconomic Modelling Bureau; Centre for Manufacturing Renewal.

Residential Facilities — Campus accommodation is available in self-catering flats or halls for approximately ⅔ of students. Snack bars, restaurants, shops and banks are provided on campus.

Cultural Opportunities — The Arts Centre complex consists of a 1325 seat Concert Hall, two theatres, a conference hall and music centre. Varied programmes of film, dance and drama are offered, and the music programme includes an International Subscription Series and performances by the resident Coull Quartet.

Sports Facilities — Two swimming pools, squash and tennis courts, facilities for most indoor and outdoor sports, Olymprene all-weather running track.

Community Links — Adult education is promoted through Open Studies courses, in-service training for teachers, and the Arden House Executive Post-Experience Centre. A 24-acre Science Park which adjoins the University was launched in 1982, and the University plays a leading role in the Coventry Consortium, which offers training services for organisations at home and abroad.

Visitors are welcome, and arrangements to see the University can be made by contacting Dr. A. Rich, University of Warwick, Coventry CV4 7AL. Tel: Coventry 24011 ext. 2708.

SCHILLER INTERNATIONAL UNIVERSITY

Schiller International University, incorporated in the United States, is an independent, international university founded in 1964, offering an American programme of higher education and conferring Associate, Bachelor and Master degrees under authority of a charter granted by the State of Missouri, U.S.A. Schiller is an accredited member of the Association of Independent Colleges and Schools, Washington D.C., U.S.A., and other educational bodies, including the British Association of Colleges for Further and Higher Education, and has reciprocal arrangements with many American universities in the United States. The campuses are located in London, Paris, Madrid, Heidelberg and Strasbourg and students may transfer from one campus to another to broaden their academic and cultural backgrounds. Potential students and their parents are welcome to visit any of our campuses any weekday during the Spring or Fall semesters to meet our staff and inspect our facilities.

COURSES OFFERED:

College Preparatory programme for grades 10-12 (American curriculum)
UNDERGRADUATE PROGRAMMES (minimum entry requirements 5 'O' levels or equivalent)
Business Administration
Associate (A.B.A.): General, Marketing, Financial Management, Management, Hotel Management.
Bachelor (B.B.A): International Business, Computer Systems Management, Financial Management, Management, Marketing, Hotel Management, Business Teacher Education, (in conjunction with New Hampshire College, U.S.A.).
Applied Sciences
Associate (A.A.S.): Pre-Engineering, Pre-Medicine.
General Studies
Associate (A.A.): Economics, European Studies, French.
Bachelor (B.A.): German, Interdepartmental Studies, International Studies, International Relations, Psychology, Spanish.
Diploma: Commercial Art, Studio Art (in conjunction with Clark University)
Law/Public Administration
Bachelor (B.P.A.) Public Administration, External L.L.B. Preparation.
GRADUATE PROGRAMMES
(Minimum entry requirements — Bachelor degree in relevant field)
Business Administration
Master (M.B.A.): Master of Business Administration.
Master (M.I.M.): Master of International Management.
General Studies
Master (M.A.): Economics, Hotel Management, International Relations, French, German, Spanish.

Schiller International University, Royal Waterloo House, 51-55 Waterloo Road, London SE1 8TX.
Telephone: (01) 928 1372.

24

MIDDLESEX POLYTECHNIC

Middlesex Polytechnic enters its second decade in 1984 with an enviable reputation for excellence and innovation in public sector higher education.

Middlesex is one of 30 polytechnics in the United Kingdom. The polytechnics, designated in the late 1960s and early 1970s, were formed by grouping together the experience and talent within colleges and institutions already engaged in higher education.

Providing the same standard of education as that provided by the universities, polytechnics offer many unusual and innovative courses not available at universities.

Originally bringing together the former Enfield College of Technology, Hendon College of Technology and Hornsey College of Art, later mergers added All Saints College, the New College of Speech and Drama, and Trent Park College of Education. Traditions from these former colleges have been successfully amalgamated into a lively institution responding to current educational demand.

Located in the north London boroughs of Barnet, Enfield and Haringey, each of the five large sites provides the setting for one or more of the faculties — the major academic communities in the Polytechnic.

The varied character of the Polytechnic is reflected in its diverse architecture which ranges from a Georgian mansion set in rolling parkland, to purpose-built campus accommodation and to large warehouse premises converted in an ultra-modern style.

The educational opportunities are comprehensive, both in the subjects offered and the ways in which these are studied. Some courses are traditional in their approach; others are unusual and even unique.

There are currently over 7000 full-time and 2000 part-time students enrolled on about 130 courses.

The Polytechnic's six faculties are: Art and Design, Business Studies and Management, Education, Performing Arts and Combined Studies, Engineering, Science and Mathematics, Humanities and Social Science.

Overseas students are particularly welcome at Middlesex Polytechnic. More than 500 overseas students are currently enrolled on courses in all areas of the Polytechnic's work.

Visitors are always welcome to visit the Polytechnic.

Information on arrangements for visits and brochures describing the Polytechnic's courses are available from:

The Information Centre,
Middlesex Polytechnic,
114 Chase Side,
London N14 5PN.
Telephone: 01-886 6599.

THAMES POLYTECHNIC

Thames Polytechnic, one of thirty polytechnics formally designated in 1970, has a long tradition of higher education. Originally it was the Woolwich Polytechnic in South East London, founded in 1890, which offered University of London degree courses for over 50 years. In 1970 the Polytechnic amalgamated with the Schools of Architecture and Surveying of the Hammersmith College of Art and Building.

Thames Polytechnic now occupies three major sites in the Woolwich town centre, South East London, as well as an attractive thirty-eight acre rural campus just outside London, in Kent.

When the original Polytechnic opened in 1890 its evening classes were attended by 500 students. This year approximately 4,500 students from all parts of Britain and many overseas countries are studying at Thames Polytechnic. A wide range of courses are offered at undergraduate, diploma and certificate level by full-time, sandwich or part-time study.

Degree courses include Computing Science, Civil, Mechanical and Electrical and Electronic Engineering, Building Surveying, Estate Management, Architecture and Materials Science. An example of a new degree course is the four year BSc (Hons) in Computer and Communication Systems which aims to help meet the demand for graduates skilled in the techniques of information technology.

All of the Polytechnic's degree courses lead to awards of the Council for National Academic Awards, a national body established in 1964 to enable institutions other than universities to offer first and Masters' degrees. These awards are equivalent in status to those of British Universities.

A large number of the Polytechnic's students study on "sandwich" courses either at degree or Higher National Diploma level. These courses are closely linked with the needs of industry, commerce, the public services and the professions, and so enable a student to study while at the same time receiving training in a relevant field. Employment and career prospects in general for students from these courses are very good.

Thames Polytechnic is a friendly place, still smaller than most Polytechnics, but with excellent facilities. As a new institution based on old traditions, it has achieved a balance between old and new and between arts and sciences.

If you would like to visit Thames Polytechnic and talk to staff and students about the subjects and courses that interest you, contact:

Mr J. Hooton, Assistant Registrar, Thames Polytechnic, Wellington Street, London SE18 6PF. Telephone: 01-854 2030 extension 207.

ARCHITECTURAL ASSOCIATION SCHOOL OF ARCHITECTURE

The AA School of Architecture is the only independent school of architecture in the UK. It was founded in response to a need for a formal education for architects, in 1847, and it has maintained that function, of being a focus for those of all ages with a strong enthusiasm for architecture and related concerns.

The School operates both as an association and as a college. There is an emphasis on public areas, such as the bar, restaurant, lecture rooms, exhibition galleries, bookshop, members' rooms where gatherings of students, tutors, administrators, members both presently studying and long involved with the AA, can be found, attending lectures by internationally known architects, visiting exhibitions or simply meeting friends. The year's events culminate in the End of Year Exhibition of work done throughout the school, on view during the last three weeks of July.

Students work at home and come into the school for teaching, discussion and criticism; they therefore need to be self-motivated and mature in their attitude to their work. The school is international, which gives an added richness to everyday contacts.

The AA School is recognised by the RIBA. The course leads therefore to exemption from RIBA Parts 1 and 2, also to the AA Diploma. It is heavily design-orientated, but technical input is supported by help within the Units and also the reserves of specialist knowledge among the membership. Students work on design projects within small groups (known as Units) of about ten to twenty, taught by one, two or three tutors; they also produce submissions in General Studies, Technical Studies and Communications. Design projects bring the young architectural student into contact with numerous other subjects and preoccupations. There are no exams, but a policy of continuous assessment involves as much day-to-day pressure and student awareness of progress made and required as in many more structured courses. It also ensures that no student passes from one year to the next without achieving the required standard of work.

Visitors are always welcome at our exhibitions. Appointments to view the School may be made at any time.

For fees and further information, please contact:

Veronica Brinton,
Admissions,
Architectural Association,
34/36 Bedford Square,
London WC1B 3ES.
Tel: 01-636 0974.

CHELSEA COLLEGE OF AERONAUTICAL & AUTOMOBILE ENGINEERING

60 years of excellence in engineering is the proud record of Chelsea College of Aeronautical and Automobile Engineering. Founded in London in 1924 to satisfy the growing demand for expertise and management skills in the rapidly developing worlds of Automobile and Aircraft Engineering, it moved in 1975 to new and spacious buildings pleasantly located at Shoreham Airport on the South Coast just 50 miles (1¼ hours by train) from London, near Brighton in Sussex.

Chelsea College has a successful history of training students from all over the world and more than 50 nationalities are represented amongst the student population.

Today, with Management courses and Transport Management Studies and special attention to the particular needs of overseas students, such as the teaching of English for engineering purposes, the College has recognised and now caters for the wider needs of the world of transport.

The balanced practical and theoretical course work together with the friendly international student environment and the very pleasant seaside location have proved a happy and successful period of totally professional training for many hundreds of students who have passed through the College.

Visitors to the College are most welcome at any time and should find interesting the well equipped workshops, laboratories and lecture rooms.

Most courses commence eight times per year.

For further information please contact:

The Registration Secretary,
Chelsea College of Aeronautical & Automobile Engineering,
Shoreham Airport,
Shoreham by Sea,
West Sussex BN4 5FJ.
Telephone: Shoreham 61198/9.
Telegrams: Aerocoll Shoreham by Sea.
Telex: 87323 FSIG

THE LONDON MONTESSORI CENTRE

Lesley Britton, who runs workshops throughout the world, gives diplomas to two students in Malaysia.

The London Montessori Centre is a training college for school leavers, teachers and parents who wish to further their knowledge of the care and educational needs of children from birth.

The courses are based on the Montessori Method of Nursery education which was developed in the early part of this century by Dr. Maria Montessori and aims to realise the maximum potential of each child through guidance in a structured environment.

The centre was founded in 1970 by Mrs. Lesley Britton as a small nursery school, which it has retained as its core while expanding into a world wide organisation meeting the adult need for further education in this field.

Lesley Britton is herself part of the dynamic tradition of British education which constantly strives to improve and up-date educational standards.

The teaching techniques at the Centre are being re-inforced continually by the latest research development and the courses are in demand throughout the world, particularly in countries where there is a growing awareness of the need for well trained child minders and day care centre staff.

Nursery (Foundation) Teaching Diploma — The basic Montessori Teacher Training Course, fundamental to a proper understanding of the Montessori philosophy and suitable for students wishing to teach nursery aged children.

Courses: Full Time (one year); Evening (one year); By correspondence.'

Primary Teaching Diploma — Suitable for students who already hold either the LMC Nursery Diploma or its equivalent. It is for students wishing to teach primary aged children.

Courses: Full Time (one year); By correspondence.

Advanced Teaching Diploma — The only course of its kind in the Montessori field of education. Suitable for students who wish to study further Montessori theory and practice it can lead to consideration for entry to some Universities.

Courses: Full Time (3 days lectures a week for one year)

Montessori Child Care Diploma — This course has been specially desinged to fill the gap which exists in child care training today. It teaches students full physical and psychological aspects of child care, while putting equal emphasis on the child's intellectual needs from birth to six years of age.

Courses: Full Time (2 years in college); By correspondence.

Primary Combination Teaching Diploma — A special refresher course for qualified teachers who wish to gain knowledge of and make use of the Montessori Method for primary children.

Course: By correspondence.

For further details please contact Mrs. J. L. Britton, London Montessori Centre, 18 Balderton St., London W1Y 1TG. Telephone 01-493 0165.

Open Day June 1, 1984. Visitors also welcome throughout the year.

English Language Schools

**and independent adult education centres
offering courses in English as a foreign language.**

School	Sex	Age	No. of students	Accommodation	Region	
ELT Banbury	M	18+	75	LSC A	C	38
Hadleigh College	F	10+	20	R L A OD	SE	39
Houghton Ed. Centre	M	16+	20	R A	SE	40
ILC	M	17+	100	L A	S	41
Kings School: Beckenham	M	16+	100	L A	LO	42
Bournemouth	M	10+	150	L A	S	42
Mitchell & Deane	M	10-16	250	LSC Su	S	42
Wimbourne	M	16+	20	L A	S	43
Pilgrims Lang. Centre	M	7+	80	L A	SE	44
Purley Sch. of Lang.	M	17+	80	S C A	SE	44
Regent Schools:	M	16+	90	LSC A	LO	45
Brighton	M	23+	40	L A	SE	46
Hove	M	16+	100	L A	SE	46
London	M	17+	200	L A	LO	46
Sels English College	M	16+	120	L A	LO	47
Swan School	M	16+	120	L A	C	48

English Language Schools

and independent adult education centres offering courses in English as a foreign language.

Please note that many of the institutions listed in other sections of this booklet also run courses in English for foreign students, particularly during the summer vacation, and similarly vacation courses in British culture.

Name of School	Sexes admitted	Ages	Student members (Normally Sept–June)	Students accepted for tuition only	Accommodation offered	Period open	Business English	Other courses in specialised English (ESP)	Teachers' courses	Secretarial courses	Arels oral	Camb. (1st Cert + Prof)	JMB Test in English	Oxford	Pitmans	RSA	TOEFL	LCCI Eng. for Commerce	Region	Page
Anglo-World:																				
Bournemouth	M	16+	100		L	A	OD	OD	•		•	•	•						S	33
Cambridge	M	16+	80	•	L	A	OD	OD			•	•		•		•	•		E	33
London	M	18+	80	•	L	A						•					•		LO	33
Oxford	M	16+	70	•	L	A	•	OD	•		•	•	•						C	33
Cambridge Centre for Languages	M	17+	60	•	L	A	•	•	•		•	•	•	•		•	•			34
Christ Church College	M	17+	80	•	L R	A	•	•	•		•	•		•	•	•	•	E	SE	35
Coventry I.E.S.C.	M	11+ }40			F	A	•	•	•		•	•		•	•	•	•	•	C	36
Edinburgh Lang.F.	M	16+ 25+ }80			L	A	•	•	•		•	•							Sc	33

33

ANGLO WORLD EDUCATION LTD

The Anglo-World Group of Companies was founded in 1963 by its present Managing Director, Gustav Scheller, and over the years has welcomed tens of thousands of overseas visitors to Britain.

Anglo-World Education has four permanent schools in Cambridge, Oxford, Bournemouth and London and, in July and August, we also organise a number of summer centres including one for younger students. Last year we welcomed students from over 70 countries world wide. Our schools are recognised as efficient by the British Council and we are members of ARELS (The Association of Recognised English Language Schools) & FELCO (Federation of English Language Course Organisations).

We should be pleased to send you our brochure containing full details of our courses and we hope to have the pleasure of welcoming you to an Anglo-World course in the future.

CAMBRIDGE ★ OXFORD ★ BOURNEMOUTH ★ LONDON

For students aged 16 years and over in Cambridge, Oxford and Bournemouth, and 18 years and over in London. Accommodation is arranged in private families.

★ Main courses commencing every 2 weeks

★ Intensive courses

★ Personal tuition courses

★ English for specific purposes

★ Examination courses

★ Supplementary courses in business and technical English

★ Holiday courses in June, July and August.

For students aged 16 years and over with college residential accommodation
★ Holiday courses in July and August.

For students aged 10-15 years with college residential accommodation
★ Junior Holiday courses in Wales.

All our schools are recognised as efficient by the British Council and we are members of ARELS/FELCO.

For further details, please write, quoting BTA/G&T: Anglo-World Education Ltd, 130-136 Poole Road, Bournemouth, Dorset, UK. Tel: (0202) 768808; Telex: 41187 AWEDUC G.

THE CAMBRIDGE CENTRE FOR LANGUAGES, SAWSTON HALL

Sawston Hall is unique for the handsomeness of its building, the beauty of its gardens and grounds (extending over 20 hectares) and the interest and drama of its history. It is one of the best preserved Tudor mansions in the country, and is historically significant because for more than 400 years it was the home of the Huddlestons, a well-known Catholic family.

Outstanding features are the Great Hall, the fine Queen Anne dining room, the Long Gallery, the Priest's Hole, the interior courtyard and the moat. The Hall is in the village of Sawston, just south of Cambridge. It is only forty minutes by car from north London.

The Centre was established to provide courses in English for non-English speakers, and also in a number of other languages for English speakers. It is intended to be a multi-national community of students helping and sharing with one another in the experience of language learning. It aims to provide teaching of university quality, but is also sufficiently small and flexible to meet the varied and immediate needs of groups and individuals.

Teaching is provided by the Centre's own well-qualified and experienced team. Members of the academic staff of the University and its Colleges also give lectures and conduct courses at Sawston Hall. The Centre offers:

- English as a Foreign Language at all levels
- Executive English
- Vacation Course in Linguistics & English Language
- English for Specific Purposes
- Professional training for Conference Interpreters.
- Junior courses for children 10-16 in separate premises

For prospectus and any further information please write to the Registrar:
The Cambridge Centre for Languages,
Sawston Hall,
Cambridge CB2 4JR.
Telephone: (0223) 835099. Telex: Camcom G 817114 for SH.

CHRIST CHURCH COLLEGE

Christ Church, set in beautiful grounds in the centre of historic Canterbury, is a College of Higher Education affiliated to the University of Kent. It is a founder member of the British Association of State Colleges in English Language Teaching (BASCELT).

The English Language Teaching Unit Offers:

★ Intensive courses for adult students and teachers of English

★ Term-time and Vacation Courses/Tailor-made courses for groups

★ M.A./Diploma in Teaching English as a Foreign Language

★ Highly qualified and experienced staff

★ Modern buildings, methods and materials — library, video, language laboratory

★ Examination preparation — e.g. Cambridge, Oxford, University of Kent Cert EFL, Chamber of Commerce

★ Tennis, squash and other sports facilities

★ Dining-hall, bar and coffee lounges

★ Accommodation on campus or with local families

Christ Church provides the ideal environment for learning English. Term-time students have every opportunity to mix with over 700 British students in other departments. Summer programmes include excursions and many different activities.

For further details and prospectus please write to:

Pat Biagi, Director, E.L.T.U.,
Christ Church College,
Canterbury, Kent CT1 1QU.
Tel: 0227 58459.
Telex: 965536 Attn. C4.

COVENTRY INTERNATIONAL ENGLISH STUDIES CENTRE

Recognised as efficient by the British Council

English Language Courses in Coventry — the Centre of England — Shakespeare's country.

Courses commence each Monday throughout the year — students may commence any Monday. Minimum stay — 2 weeks. All ages — all levels. Family groups. Various courses e.g. English for Conversation, Examinations, Pleasure and Leisure. Special English for Managers, Engineers, Secretaries, Doctors.
Accommodation in selected private English family, single bedroom.

The School, established in 1971, is in a Georgian building within the Cathedral precincts overlooking a small park, just two minutes walk from the City Centre. There are 10 classrooms, T.V. Room, Library, Common Room, Language Laboratory and administration offices. The School has a full time Accommodation and Welfare Officer who is responsible for the personal welfare of the students. General English and Examination courses are available; students may opt for either 15 or 25 hours tuition per week. The School is open all the year except for public holidays. Courses are available for students of all ages. A modern Sports Centre, including an Olympic size swimming pool is nearby as are also facilities for most sports including tennis, golf and horseriding.

Coventry is a small, interesting university city with contrasting ancient and modern architecture and offering most of the shopping and leisure facilities of a larger city. Situated in the Centre of England in "Shakespeareland" it is ideal for sightseeing excursions and one hour ten minutes by train from London.

Secretarial Courses — leading to recognised secretarial qualifications.
Duration — one academic year.

Creative Tours — tailored excursions for mature visitors to places of literary, architectural and pleasurable interest throughout England, Wales and Scotland.
Duration of Tours — 5, 7 or 10 days as required.

All enquiries to:

The Director,
Coventry International English Studies Centre,
9 Priory Row,
Coventry.
Tel: (0203) 23379 23340

THE EDINBURGH LANGUAGE FOUNDATION

The Edinburgh Language Foundation is an independent teaching body, recognised by the British Council, and dedicated to the teaching of English to clients from overseas, particularly where there are special objectives in the language learning. For example, a main focus of our work is the preparation of overseas students — postgraduate, undergraduate and college — to take up their places in UK universities or colleges. These 'study-skills' courses, which are very popular, illustrate the educational philosophy of the Foundation. The programme offers daily English language enrichment at the appropriate level, provides teaching in the skills required for survival and success in the university or college and offers specialist teaching of the English of the students' special subject interest.

ELF has built up, over several years, a wide range of special materials and teaching resources for study skills and specialist English. Our staff are expert in the techniques associated with this work. One of our special areas of interest, for instance, is *English for Medicine*. Others are *English for Science and Technology* (including oil-related engineering). We have special materials and experience in engineering (mechanical and electrical) and in electronics. A special sector of our teaching provides courses in *English for Maritime and Naval Studies*.

A feature of the work of ELF is the programme of courses we offer for teachers from overseas who wish to refresh their language and their methodology during the summer, or at other times of the year. These courses, entitled *Teaching English: the Communicative Approach* provide two and three-week modules of study on specified dates each summer.

At the heart of our work lies our teaching of English itself. We can offer courses in general English enrichment at any time during the year and at various intensities. A special feature of this part of our teaching is the *ELF Summer School*, offering a blend of English classes and daily cultural and recreational activities assisted by our staff.

The reputation of the Foundation has been built up as a result of our careful planning of courses and development of materials. The staff are highly qualified teachers with extensive overseas experience. We are always ready to help clients to plan courses to suit their particular needs.

We arrange family accommodation for our students, and help them to enjoy Edinburgh during their stay.

Our brochure and information sheets and further assistance can be had by writing to: Dr William B. Currie, Principal, Edinburgh Language Foundation, 11 Great Stuart Street, Edinburgh EH3 7TS. Telephones 031-225 8785, 031-225 9886. Telex: (1) 72165 ELF.

Recognised by the British Council

Felco

E.L.T.
BANBURY

ELT Banbury (U.K.) and ELT International (overseas) cannot be described as language schools in the traditional sense. They represent a comprehensive English Language servicing organisation offering:-

★ Consultancy

★ In-service training

★ Teacher training

★ Teacher recruitment

★ English language schools

★ Short and long-term overseas on-site assignments.

A clue to this total service to communication in English language lies in the initials ELT — English Language Training. Training is the key word. ELT Banbury exists as part of wider training programmes. If it offers courses to Shell process operators from Saudi Arabia, to French waterwork engineers, to Plessey radar technicians from Ecuador, it is because English is the language of communication in the transfer of technology. In a word, ELT Banbury specialises in providing the English Language skills needed in international training.

★ English for Technicians and Technologists
★ Video Course
★ English for Aviation Science
★ English for Computer Staff

★ English for Business and Management
★ English for the Medical Profession
★ English for Engineers
★ English for Banking

ELT Banbury is also the centre of the ELT International operations with teachers and teaching centres in countries as diverse as Abu Dhabi, Bahrain, China, France, Germany, Hong Kong, Indonesia, Italy, Saudi Arabia and Thailand. Teachers are recruited and briefed at ELT Banbury before taking up posts overseas. Many stay with ELT International and transfer from country to country within the ELT group.

ELT Banbury is synonymous for its structured programmes, the excellence of its teaching, the care and quality of its services. ELT Banbury is a name in the training world.

For further information please contact: Dr. T. J. Gerighty, ELT Banbury, 20 Horsefair, Banbury, Oxfordshire. Telex: 83544 ELTBAN. Telephone: 3480 or 3502.

HADLEIGH COLLEGE

Residential School of English for girls
Open all the year round, warm family atmosphere.

Hadleigh is one of the relatively few Schools of English in Britain for girls only. The Principals live at the school with their young family, and the students receive their personal supervision. The school is proud of the high reputation it has built up throughout the world.

Hadleigh is conveniently situated in Cliftonville, a pleasant seaside resort near the Channel ports of Ramsgate, Dover and Folkestone and within easy reach of London. It is an ideal place not only to learn English but also to discover some of Britain's varied and colourful heritage. The famous city of Canterbury with its beautiful Cathedral and quaint old streets, the historic castles of Dover and Leeds and the picturesque villages of Kent all lie within a short distance of our school and can be visited on our free weekly excursions, together with further places of interest such as Windsor Castle, Brighton and, of course, London.

The school offers 35 residential places. Students can also live with carefully selected English families should the Principal decide this would be more beneficial. Our classes are small and courses are available at all levels. All our teachers are well qualified and experienced and excellent results are obtained in our examinations.

We prepare students for the Pitmans, RSA, Cambridge First Certificate and Proficiency examinations in English as a Foreign Language, the Pitmans examinations in Shorthand and Typing and boarding school or college entrance. Girls are accepted from the age of 10.

The social life offered by the school is interesting and varied and includes visits to theatres and cinemas, as well as the excursions mentioned above.

For further information please contact

The Principal,
Hadleigh School of English,
15 Warwick Road,
Cliftonville,
Kent CT9 2JX.
Tel: Thanet 23555.
Telegrams: Hadleigh-Margate.

HOUGHTON EDUCATION CENTRE

Situated in idyllic English countryside, Houghton Education Centre is approximately 70 miles from London and 8 miles from the historic city of Winchester.

First mentioned in William the Conqueror's great Domesday Book of 1086, North Houghton Manor was re-built in 1706 and became the home of the present family in 1950. The beautiful spacious gardens and park surrounding the manor, the swimming pool, the tennis courts, the croquet lawn, and a host of other amenities have welcomed foreign students since they first came here in 1960.

Houghton Education Centre is an exclusive tutorial establishment devoted not only to the study of the English language, but also to providing students with a unique opportunity to become acquainted with the English cultural heritage and way of life.

Numbers of students are deliberately restricted to maintain quality of teaching, with about 15 students studying during the academic year and around 20 attending the Summer courses in July and August from the age of sixteen upwards.

Teaching is adapted to the requirements of each particular group, usually 4 or 5 students, with individual tuition given wherever necessary. Courses are offered leading to the Pitman language examinations or the Cambridge First and Proficiency Certificates in English. Individual coaching is also given in 'O' level subjects to students seeking higher educational studies in the U.K.

A happy family atmosphere prevails at Houghton Education Centre and all students are encouraged to widen their outlook on life by participating in topical discussions, often at mealtimes, and by learning different cultures and customs through acquaintance and mutual sharing.

Houghton Education Centre's Open Day is on 1st July and a welcome is extended to all visitors to attend this event.

Houghton Education Centre, North Houghton Manor, Stockbridge, Hants, SO20 6LF. Tel: 0264 810633.

INTERNATIONAL LANGUAGE CENTRE

ILC was founded in 1968 and now has centres in Salisbury, London, Paris, Kuwait, Tokyo, Osaka and Nagoya, with a centre opening shortly in Singapore. ILC is a member of ARELS and FELCO and is recognised as efficient by the British Council.

ILC employs 300 staff around the world and they are carefully selected for their ability, personality and powers of communiction. The education staff is supported by a highly professional and experienced administrative staff.

The Group provides a wide range of Executive, Group, Specialist, Teacher Training and Holiday Courses. By virtue of our experience and expertise, we can offer specially tailored training programmes anywhere in the world.

For students coming to the United Kingdom we can offer a wide selection of courses. Our permanent school is situated in the cathedral city of Salisbury, 120kms. south west of London, in one of the most beautiful regions of England. Salisbury is convenient for Heathrow and from the channel ports for those who wish to arrive by car.

The Executive Centre offers short intensive courses for businessmen and professional people who must make the best possible use of their time. Courses are either in small groups or on a one to one basis. Accommodation can be organised with professional families in the area or in local hotels.

The General English School, which is also in Salisbury, is designed for students who wish to take rather longer and less intensive courses from 1-6 months. Classes are at various levels with a maximum number of 15.

Courses in most foreign languages are arranged on an individual basis in our London Centre, in addition to one-to-one English courses.

ILC also has Holiday Course Centres in London, Cambridge and Salisbury, which are designed for those who wish to enjoy their holiday, but, at the same time, improve their English. Accommodation is either in residences or with host families. The Modern English Literature course takes place in Cambridge during the summer.

As an integral part of all our courses in England, there is a comprehensive social programme of excursions, pub crawls, discos and cocktail parties;

Visitors are welcome to visit our Salisbury Language Centre on Wednesdays throughout May, June and July, or, at any other times by appointment.

For further information please contact: Executive Courses, General English Courses, Teacher Training Courses, International Language Centre, (UK) Ltd, The Old House, 3 Rougement Close, Salisbury, Wilts SP1 1LY. Tel: (722) 337897. Telex 477019 ASR G. Holiday Courses, Foreign Language Courses. International Language Centre (UK) Ltd, 9 Cavendish Square, London W1M 9DD. Tel: (1)580 4351. Telex 299196 ILCHQ G.

THE KING'S GROUP OF ENGLISH LANGUAGE & TECHNICAL SCHOOLS

The King's Group consists of 4 schools. King's School of English, Bournemough and King's College of Further Education are situated on the beautiful south coast, 95 minutes by train from London. King's London is situated in the suburbs, 20 minutes by train from London, and King's Wimborne is situated in a small historic town, 16 kilometres from Bournemouth.

The King's Group in its four schools offers a wide range of courses to meet the needs of different types of students. These are:-

1. **King's School of English, Bournemouth, (Minimum age 16 years)**
— Main Courses — 24 lessons per week; 6 levels from beginners to advanced. — Examination Courses
— The school runs special courses for the following
— Cambridge First Certificate — 16 weeks, 24 lessons per week.
— Cambridge Proficiency — 24 weeks, 24 lessons per week
— Easter Special Course — 20 lessons per week, duration 2, 3 or 4 weeks.
— Summer Special Course — 20 lessons per week, duration 2 — 10 weeks, courses in June, July and August.

2. **King's College of Further Education, (Minimum age 16 years)**
— G.C.E. 'A' level courses in Applied Mathematics, Pure Mathematics, Chemistry and Physics. Duration 1 or 2 years.
— Secretarial Training Courses — Duration 1, 2 or 3 terms (1 year)
— Business Training Courses — Duration 4 12-week terms beginning 2/7/84.
— Computer Training Courses — Duration 4 12-week terms beginning 2/7/84.
— Short Intensive Courses — 30 lessons per week, duration minimum 2 weeks, maximum 8 weeks. Courses run all the year round.
— English for Specific Groups — depending on requirments of client.

3. **King's School of English, Wimborne (10-16 years)**
— Junior Courses — 20 lessons per week, duration minimum 2 weeks, maximum 50 weeks; courses run all the year round.

4. **King's School of English, London (Minimum age 16 years)**
— Intensive courses — 30 lessons per week; January — June, September — December. Minimum 4 weeks, maximum 24 weeks.
— Summer Short Intensive Courses — 24 lessons per week plus a programme of evening lectures. July and August.
— Summer Special Courses — 16 lessons per week; duration 2-7 weeks. July and August.

All of our schools provide carefully selected family accommodation. With the exception of King's Wimborne, accommodation is part-board i.e. breakfast, evening meal during the week and 3 meals at weekends. At King's Wimborne accommodation is full-board throughout the week. Our own Travel Department organises excursions to many fascinating places in the U.K. as well as Europe. King's Group, 58 Braidley Road, Bournemouth BH2 6LD. Tel: (0202) 293535. Telex: 41205 KNGBTH G.

MITCHELL
AND DEANE

Robin Mitchell, B.A. has much experience of organizing and teaching English Language Course in which she has been involved since 1975. She has an Honours Degree in English Literature from Sussex University.

This year under the banner of the British Tourist Authority's Heritage '84 promotion Mitchel and Deane have devised English Craft and Heritage Courses.

"These courses are designed for people who like combining leisure and learning and who also enjoy the peaceful setting of village life and beautiful Sussex countryside," said Mrs. Robin Mitchell, Directo of Mitchell and Deane, who devised the holidays.

"The informal village atmosphere and intimate group talks and discussions — six people to a course — are an essential part of the holidays and one of the reasons they are so different," Mrs. Mitchel explained.

On craft courses only six students are taken each week, to learn pottery, weaving, spinning, jewellery making, patchwork or woodcraft, working alongside professional craftsmen in their own workshops and studios. All the craftsmen-tutors are members of the Guild of Sussex Craftsmen and it is a rare opportunity to work with highly skilled — sometimes internationally famous — craftsmen.

Study courses include Sussex Life and Institutions, with lectures and visits to places of historic interest, tracing the life and culture of bygone Sussex; Interior Design, covering the whole spectrum of design from medieval timber-frame buildings to modern uses of colour and texture; and English Farmhouse Cookery, when culinary secrets and regional recipes are tried and shared.

"We expect the courses will be particularly popular with overseas visitors," Robin Mitchell said, speaking from her office in Steyning, one of Sussex's most historic villages.

"For anyone whose English is less advanced, the courses can be combined with English language classes, and for anyone who prefers to stay in a country hotel we can arrange hotel accommodation."

We have an Open Day every Thursday, but visitors are welcome at any other time by appointment.

Mitchell and Deane,
29 High Street,
Steyning,
West Sussex BN4 3GG.
Telephone Steyning (0903) 815984.

PILGRIMS LANGUAGE COURSES

Roedean College, Brighton, one of Pilgrims' centres for Language in Action courses.

We started Pilgrims Language Courses in 1974. That year, there were 106 students on a Summer School at the University of Kent at Canterbury. Now, there are 1800 students, 5 Summer Schools, a full time Executive Training Centre, a Publishing Division, a Teacher Training Division and a Research and Development Unit. Pilgrims is recognised as efficient by the British Council and is a member of ARELS/FELCO.

Pilgrims is distinguished from other organisations by:

★ our use of teaching specialists from around the world. For each course we choose professionals with relevant qualifications and experience. Our teaching is exciting, creative and imaginative.

★ our teams of teachers, social organisers and administrative staff working together to create a friendly ambience in carefully chosen course locations.

★ the application of a wide range of teaching methods to achieve the practical learning objectives of each course.

★ the active contribution made by every participant to the success of our courses.

★ our guarantee of confidence and quality: 'If you are not satisfied with your course, you may leave at the end of the first week. Pilgrims will refund the full fees for that course.'

The Courses

Summer Courses for adults — 2- and 4-week courses held at the University of Kent at Canterbury. Highly-motivated men and women are offered a choice of two intensive programmes: 4½ or 6 full hours tuition each day in groups of average 8 participants. The highly imaginative teaching programmes are supplemented by special interest seminar work and an integrated social programme involving English people. We offer accommodation in comfortable single study bedrooms in a modern University college and first-rate sports facilities.

Executive Courses — courses of Individual and Group-3 tuition held throughout the year in our Canterbury training centre. A 6½ hour daily programme with genuine personal attention ensures rapid progress for the participants, who are mostly sponsored by companies or institutions. We provide accommodation with English people in business and professional life.

Language in Action Courses for Children (7-11 and 12-17 years) — 3 week courses, held in July and August, with residential accommodation at Roedean College (Brighton) and family accommodation in Canterbury. We provide small classes and personal attention for each child. English is taught in real situations by skilled and sympathetic teachers throughout the day.

For further information on courses and services offered by Pilgrims contact:
John Miles, Pilgrims Language Courses, 8 Vernon Place, Canterbury, Kent CT1 3YG. England. Tel: (0227) 69127. Telex: 965536.

PURLEY LANGUAGE CENTRE

English for Foreigners and Secretarial Courses have been held in Purley for over fifty years. The Language Centre is housed in a pleasant modern building in the heart of Purley, a residential town some twenty miles south of central London. Gatwick Airport is only thirty minutes by direct train or twenty minutes by road. For those arriving at Heathrow there is a bus or underground train to Victoria Station where main line trains to Purley may be caught. Trains also run to Purley from Charing Cross, Waterloo and London Bridge.

English for Foreigners

Students of all ages and nationalities are welcomed throughout the year, except Christmas when the School is closed for two weeks.

Students may attend General English Courses for 15 or 25 hours per week. Both written and oral work are covered and the students are given an idea of the English way of life, institutions, literature and history. Typewriting, Book-keeping and Commercial Correspondence are often undertaken by students with a reasonable knowledge of English. Visual Aids such as cassettes, records, slides television and video are used.

Vacation Courses consisting of tuition, supervised sports activities and excursions are organised for groups, so that members are looked after all day.

Secretarial Courses

For students with at least an 'O' level in English Language, CSE Grade 1 or equivalent there is a Full Secretarial Course lasting 24 weeks or 36 weeks, and beginning in January, at Easter and in September. This Course includes Typewriting, Audio Typewriting, Shorthand, Word Processing, Secretarial Duties, Book-keeping and Commercial Correspondence.

A very intensive 15-week Secretarial Course is available for Graduates.

Accommodation (full-board) is arranged in carefully selected local host families. Hotel accommodation is available in the vicinity.

Tuition is given by qualified staff experienced in teaching English to Foreigners and/or Secretarial Subjects. Students are prepared for examinations held by Cambridge University (First Certificate and Proficiency) the Royal Society of Arts, The London Chamber of Commerce, Pitman Examinations Institute, University of London and University of Oxford.

Visitors are welcome at Purley. Contact Miss P W Kent, Principal, Purley Language Centre and Purley School of Commerce and Languages, 14 Brighton Road, Purley, Surrey CR2 3AB. Telephone: 01-660 2568/5060, 01-668 8778/4022. Telex 943763 Crocom G ref PUR.

46

REGENT SCHOOLS

Regent School, London W.1.

The REGENT SCHOOL OF ENGLISH — a leading name in language teaching — was founded over twenty years ago. We now offer a complete range of English Language Training Programmes:

★ **General English and Examination Courses** in London W1 and in Hove/Brighton.

★ **Executive English Training** in London W1 and in Brighton.

★ **Summer Holiday Courses** for adults and juniors in six centres around England (London, Oxford, Exeter, Newbury, Weymouth and Hatfield).

★ **Teachers' Courses.**

★ **On site specialised English Language Training world-wide.**

For further information please contact our Head Office:

4 Percy Street,
London W1P 9FA.
Tel: 01-636 9444/5. Telex: 21466 REGENT G

Approved by the BRITISH COUNCIL

Felco

 # SELS COLLEGE

English in Covent Garden

Sels is a well established School of English situated in one of the most historic and lively parts of London, Covent Garden, surrounded by such famous places as the Royal Opera House, the National Gallery, the British Museum, and the Royal Courts of Justice. It is only ten minutes away from Picadilly Circus and Trafalgar Square. The School occupies clean spacious premises at the junction of Long Acre and Bow Street. It is recognised by the British Council and is a member of ARELS/FELCO.

Sels is a warm friendly college with emphasis on success. It was founded with the specific aim of teaching English in small groups of 6 to 9 students, or on a one-to-one basis. Students can study full or part-time, for short or long periods, from complete beginners to advanced Cambridge Proficiency. The College offers tailor-made courses to executives and prepares students for academic studies.

Sels College students, who come from all over the world and range in age from 16 to 60, include doctors, diplomats, engineers and housewives. All the courses are intensive and demanding. Assignments are set at the end of each session and there is a monthly progress test. Students who complete their course successfully are awarded a Certificate of Merit.

The College is directed by Mr Y. Syde, who has thirty years' experience of teaching English at all levels from beginners to University, both in England and abroad. "We regard our students as our guests; their welfare and success is our main concern. They come to us for more than just English, they want the experience of living and studying a language and culture that is appreciated all over the world. We do our best to give them a taste of English heritage," says the Principal.

Open days are held each Thursday throughout the year and visitors are welcome to tour the college and meet the Principal.

Sels College London,
64/65 Long Acre,
Covent Garden,
London WC2E 9JH.

Tel: 240 2581. Telex: 268312 WESCOM G ATTN SELSCOL.

Principal: Y Syde BA, BSc(Econ), MEd, LTCL, Dips TEFL, EdRes,
Hist Lit, Intl Affrs, FIL, Barrister.

THE SWAN SCHOOL OF ENGLISH

Recognised as efficient by The British Council

The Swan School of English was founded in 1965 by Michael and Hazel-Ann Swan, both teachers of English as a Foreign Language. Today it is still an independent, British-owned, "family" school, not part of any larger organisation, concentrating on good standards of teaching/learning, and providing courses for seriously-motivated students. The School occupies two large Victorian houses in North Oxford. It is on main bus routes, about one kilometre from the city centre and from shops, restaurants and sporting facilities. There are twelve classrooms, attractive gardens and spacious student common rooms, recreational and private study facilities, including a library and a listening centre. The School offers general English Language courses for overseas students all year round, plus courses for overseas teachers of English in the summer and by arrangement. There are long courses (average 10 weeks) in Spring, Summer, Autumn and Winter; three-week intensive courses, with aural/oral emphasis, throughout the year; and three-week teachers' courses in July and August. The School has a capacity of about 120 students, with an average of 9-12 students in each class (8-10 on Teachers' courses). Tuition is from 9.30 to 4.30 daily, comprising 23 hours per week (Friday afternoons are free for sport, excursions, etc.). The library and listening centre are available for students' use at all other times from 8.30 to 5.30 daily. Optional classes such as business, literature, translation and current affairs are arranged according to demand. Social organisers provide a full programme of excursions and entertainments, and the Accommodation Secretary arranges family accommodation within walking or cycling distance of the School (self-catering also available in July and August).

Dates for 1984 are as follows:

Long courses: starting 10th January, 13th March, 24th April, 25th July and 2nd October.

Short courses: starting 31st January, 21st February, 13th March, 3rd April, 8th May, 29th May, 19th June, 3rd July, 24th July, 14th August, 4th September, 30th October, 20th November and 11th December.

Teachers' courses: starting 3rd July, 24th July and 14th August.

Write for further information to:

Dept. GT,
The Swan School of English,
111 Banbury Road,
Oxford OX2 6JX
or visit us personally if you come to Oxford.

The School Fees Dilemma!

10 YEARS FROM NOW HE COULD BE COSTING YOU £10,000 A YEAR

According to a recent I.S.I.S. Census school fees were still rising at 10% in 1982, faster than the rate of inflation.

It is a worrying thought that even at present levels of inflation the average cost of private school fees could be as high as £10,000 a year in 10 years time. Put another way that could mean a cost of at least £50,000 to put a child through public school.

Towry Law will tell you how you can save around 50% of that amount by investing now in a school fees scheme that is totally free of income and capital gains tax and can also have capital transfer tax advantages.

Whatever the age of your child or grandchild, ask Towry Law. We can help you to make substantial savings. So fill in the coupon now for an individual quotation without obligation.

Ask Towry Law

Recommended by **ISIS**

Independent Schools
Information Service

Established 25 years • Specialists in School Fees Planning

Business Schools and Secretarial Colleges

Please note that a number of the colleges and schools listed in the other sections of this booklet also offer secretarial courses.

BLACKBURN SECRETARIAL COLLEGE

The ability to recognise a need within a community and over a much wider area beyond it, coupled with the necessary skills and driving power to meet it in a practical way and adapt it to individual requirements, add up to the rare genius possessed by Mrs. Jennifer Pejcinovic, founder and Executive Principal of Blackburn Secretarial College.

A highly skilled proficient staff, most of whom have been with the College during its lengthy term of existence — it is now in its 15th year — are led by Principal Mrs Ann Cheshire who has been there for around 13 years. Her main, and extremely important specialised subject has been English with the Foreign Students. Now, more and more she is involved with the administrative side, Mrs Pejcinovic having delegated much of the responsibility to her.

Should you require any details of courses held at the College either write or telephone. Brochures of courses and how each can be adapted to suit the needs of every individual student, whatever their age or ultimate goal, are immediately obtainable.

Although the Prospectus lists the regular courses, each can be adapted to individual requirements and extra or alternative subjects can be taken, in conjunction with them or separately, on a full time, part time, or shorter term basis. Fees are adapted accordingly.

Such degrees of flexibility are rare in educational establishments which cater for educational and business training, geared not only to traditional and current office and commercial practice but already answering the challenges of the rapidly developing microchip age and the newest types of commercial equipment such technological advances are constantly being introduced.

Students are equipped with skills to meet the challenging changes of all these technological advances with confidence and the ability to adapt to them.

The clear sighted vision of Jennifer Pejcinovic, and the wholehearted co-operation of her loyal, happy staff have built up the excellent reputation of Blackburn Secretarial College to its high degree of excellence, making it not only an asset to Blackburn but to many other towns and places abroad forming the wide area of student intake.

★ Intensive Secretarial Courses

★ Full and Part-time courses for all ages

★ Junior Commercial Course for students of 14 years of age and over

★ Courses in English as a Foreign Language

For further details contact:

Blackburn Secretarial College,
4 East Park Road,
Blackburn,
Lancs.
Telephone (0254) 60656. Telex 63474.

GREENWICH COLLEGES

INTRODUCE

★ **The Centre for Business Studies** — Masters Degree, First Degrees & Professional Courses in a full range of Business and Management Subjects. From September, January and June each year.

★ **ELS International Language Centre** — 4, 8, 12, 16 & 20 week Standard Courses. Intensive Executive Courses — 2, 4 & 6 weeks. English for Specific Purposes (ESP) — Duration by arrangement.

★ **Greenwich Tutorial College** — GCE at Ordinary and Advanced Level in a full range of Science and Arts subjects. From September and January each year.

Greenwich is the birthplace of Britain's sea faring tradition. For many centuries its life has been dominated by the world outside our shores. There could thus hardly be a more appropriate location for Greenwich Colleges with students from forty nations and international recognition for the many courses they provide. The Colleges are continuously developing their courses and facilities and they maintain a high standard of tuition, making them one of Britain's leading group of independent colleges of higher education.

Facilities include: — Language, Science and Computer laboratories, Accommodation Service, Airport Reception, Library, Sports Facilities, Student Restaurant, Modern well equipped lecture rooms, social events.

For a Prospectus write, telephone or telex:

**The Registrar
Greenwich Colleges
Meridian House
Royal Hill
Greenwich, London SE10 8RJ.
Telephone: 01-853 4484
Telex: 8953233 ELSLON G**

LONDON SCHOOL OF INSURANCE

As you read this brochure...

countless disasters will have affected the lives of human beings. The disasters may have been either physical, financial or emotional or all three. While emotional and physical disasters are hard to correct, financial hardship can be reduced or even removed with insurance.

When you consider the range of things which can go wrong, then you can have some idea of the part you can play as a professional insurer. But you need professional training.

The United Kingdom is a world centre of insurance. The Chartered Insurance Institute (The CII) is the central educational and professional body for all engaged or employed in insurance. THE LONDON SCHOOL OF INSURANCE is currently the only institution in Europe offering full-time courses leading to CII qualifications, which are respected worldwide.

The CII examinations rank at three levels. Preparation for all three levels exists at The LSI, with the addition of Foundation Courses for those students who do not have the initial qualifications.

The LSI was started in 1982 in consultation with The CII and with The Glasgow College of Technology, whose full time CII courses ended in March 1984. The lectures come from within the industry (some retired, some working in or running their own insurance or broking firms) and from education (The University of London, London Polytechnics and Technical Colleges). Additionally, there is a guest lectureship programme, when experts in particular fields of insurance or noted insurance teachers visit The LSI.

Since insurance is an international activity, The LSI has already developed links overseas. It is presently involved in the development of a school of insurance in the Middle East.

The LSI offers the best foundation for a career which offers both a vital service and superb career opportunities.

Open days: Every Friday in July and August.

For further information please contact:

500 Chesham House,
150 Regent Street,
London W1R 5FA
Telephone: 01-831 7958
Telex: 261426 ADFONE G

ST. GODRIC'S COLLEGE

St. Godric's College gives training in English, Secretarial and Business courses. The College is internationally recognised and attracts students from over 50 countries. Established in 1929, St. Godric's is now the largest college of its kind in Britain, with a population of some 400 students, approximately half of whom are from overseas. High quality training, the College family atmosphere and its location in London combine to make a course at St. Godric's a special and rewarding experience.

On the English Courses students are taught by tutors who are all university graduates and are specially qualified to teach English as a Foreign Language. Students are carefully streamed, they work in small classes from Preliminary level up to Cambridge Proficiency. Those with adequate English may then take further courses, either the Combined Secretarial and English Course (3 terms), the entry requirement being Cambridge First Certificate, or the Business Studies Course (3 terms), which requires Proficiency or equivalent.

English-speaking students have a wide choice of secretarial courses. The Intensive Course lasts 6 months. The Executive Course, combines secretarial training with business studies and lasts one year. The French Secretarial Course and Liberal Studies and Secretarial Course are both 2 years. The latter is a blend of secretarial training with liberal studies, fashion and cookery.

Our Business Studies Course is an intensive and practical year of study covering subject matter, including computer training, normally found in much longer courses. It is designed especially for those who wish to enter small or family businesses.

The College provides residence for students who wish it. Accommodation consists of 7 large family houses occupied by English and overseas students together, where English is the common language and life-long friendships are made. Each house is cared for by a Lady Warden whose main responsibility is the happiness and welfare of her students. Catering is supervised by a professional London firm.

St. Godric's College is located in Hampstead, a charming and attractive area in London close to shops, sports facilities and Hampstead Heath. Hampstead has the atmosphere of a village, yet it takes only 20 minutes to reach the City centre with its wealth of theatres, museums, art galleries and shopping at world-renowned stores.

For further information about our Courses and our Heritage Scholarship Scheme, contact:

The Registrar,
2 Arkwright Road,
London, NW3 6AD.
Telephone: 01-435 9831. Telex: 25589.

Ask about our College Video.

WEST LONDON COLLEGE

West London College specialises in intensive tuition for overseas students who wish to acquire internationally recognised UK qualifications leading to a professionl career or to university. Tutors combine practical experience with the highest academic honours and have at their disposal the latest advanced teaching aids. Special care is taken to introduce students to the wealth of cultural and leisure opportunities with which London and the UK are so richly endowed.

We offer Courses covering the following subjects:-

Business Training

All our Courses lead to internationally recognised Professional Qualifications including the MBA (Masters Degree in Business Administration).
MARKETING — IM (Institute of Marketing)
ACCOUNTANCY — ACCA (Association of Certified Accountants)
BANKING — AIB (Institute of Bankers)
COMPUTER TRAINING — ABAC (Association of Computer Professionals)
MANAGEMENT — IAM, ABE, BMC, CPM
CATERING — City & Guilds 706 I and II, 781 and 794

Many Other Subjects

GCE and English as a Foreign Language.

U.S.A. Courses

West London College also offers summer courses at London to USA University students. The courses lead to Certificates giving 'Degree Credits'.

Scholarships and Bursaries

Up to six full one year's tuition scholarships will be awarded annually. The courses offered are designed to prepare students for the Professional Qualifications in Business Studies.

College Recognition

When choosing your college it is essential to know whether a college is 'Recognised'. West London College is 'Recognised' throughout the educational world and is a member of ARBS (Association for the Recognition of Business Schools). We are also proud to announce that we run courses in association with a leading British Government owned College.

Prospectus

Provided you have the necessary educational qualifications or are willing to prepare for them we shall be happy to send you our prospectus, or if you are in London, better still, come in and meet us.

538 Avon House, 360 Oxford Street, London W1, England. Tel No: 01-492 1841/2.

THE INDEPENDENT SECRETARIAL TRAINING ASSOCIATION

ISTA was founded in 1973 and is an association of private, independent secretarial training colleges.

ISTA's aims are to maintain the highest standards of training and professional conduct in every aspect of business education.

Why Choose an ISTA College?

Most of the best private secretarial colleges are members of ISTA, whose concern for such points as staff-student ratio, suitability of courses for candidates accepted, and training for external examinations means that high standards in training are maintained.

Members of ISTA share common aims and ideals and work closely together but each college is independent and the membership offers a very wide choice of courses to students.

The information given in the summary is intended only as a general guide to colleges, to whom specific enquiries should be addressed. College prospectuses will be supplied on request to Principals who will arrange interviews and answer queries. Admission and information is obtained by direct application to the college concerned — not through the Independent Secretarial Training Association.

Please write for information and list of member colleges to:-

The Secretary,
Independent Secretarial Training Association,
16 Marlborough Crescent,
London W4 1HF.

Independent Colleges of Further Education and Tutorial Colleges

North Midlands Tutorial College	M	30	●	F S 15+	●	●	●	●		C. England	76
Oxford Academy	M	120	●	F 16+	●	●	●	●		C. England	77
Padworth College	G	150	●	R 15+	●	●	●			S. England	78
St. Aldates College	M	300	●	F S 15+	●	●	●	●		C. England	79
St. Giles College	M	55	●	FSR 16+	●	●				S. E. England	80
St. Joseph's Hall	M	45	●	F R 17+	●	●				C. England	81
St. Matthew's Tutorial College	M	150	●	FRS 16+	●	●	●			C. England	82
Stake Farm	G	45	●	F R 16+	●	●				S. E. England	83
Symondsbury College	M	40	●	F R 15+	●	●	●			S. W. England	84
University Tutorial College	M	500	●	R 16+	●				●	London	85
Wessex Tutors	M	40	●	F S 16+	●	●	●		●	S. England	86
Winchester Tutorial College	M	100	●	F S 18+	●	●				S. England	87
Wolsey Hall Tutorial College	M	100	●	F S 18+	●	●	●		●	C. England	88
Woodhill Tutorial College	M	40	●	F R 14+	●	●	●	●	●	E. England	89

Abbreviations used:

G — Girls only
M — Mixed
F — Accommodation with families
R — College Residence
S — Self-catering
EFL — English as a Foreign Language
SCE — Scottish Certificate of Education
CIFE — Conference for Independent Further Education.

Note:

Summer School — This refers to summer vacation courses in English as a Foreign Language and British Culture, or alternatively pre-sessional courses in GCE subjects.

Independent Colleges of Further Education and Tutorial Colleges

Name of College	Sexes accepted	No. of students	Day students	Accommodation available	Age of students	GCE O Level/SCE	GCE A Level	Oxbridge Entrance	All year EFL courses	Summer School	Secretarial courses	Region	Page
Basil Paterson College	M	180	●	F	15+	●	●	●				Scotland	62
Beechlawn Tutorial College	G	75	●	F S	16+	●	●	●				C. England	63
Bosworth Tutors	M	60	●	R	15+	●	●					C. England	64
Capital College	M	150	●	F S	16+	●	●	●	●	●	●	London	65
Clymping College	M	40	●	F R	14+	●	●		●	●	●	S. E. England	66
Connaught College	M	110	●	F R	15+	●	●	●	●	●	●	S. W. England	67
Davies's College — Hove	M	300	●	F	14+	●	●	●	●	●	●	S.E. England	68
Davies's College — London	M	600	●	F S	16+	●	●	●				London	69
Edinburgh Tutorial College	M	40	●	F S	16+	●	●		●			Scotland	70
Greylands College	M	80	●	R	15+	●	●		●	●		S. England	71
Harrogate Tutorial College	M	25	●	F S	15+	●	●					N. England	72
International Tutorial College	M	70	●	F	16+	●	●	●	●	●	●	S. W. England	73
Irwin Academy	M	75	●	R S	15+	●	●	●				C. England	74
Milestone Schools	M	120	●	F	16+	●	●	●	●	●	●	London	75

THE BASIL PATERSON COLLEGE

The Basil Paterson College is situated Abercromby Place in the centre of Edinburgh, in two adjoining Georgian houses overlooking pleasant gardens.

The College was founded in 1929. It is now part of an organisation which includes a tutorial college offering GCE 'O' and 'A' level courses, a secretarial college (known as 'Dugdale McAdam's), and a School of English. This format is particularly useful for overseas students who are not native speakers of English, as they can combine English learning with courses in other subjects within the same building. From October to June approximately 130 of the 220 or so students in the college are British, so all overseas students have a good opportunity of meeting young British people.

The College is relatively small and is still in family ownership. The atmosphere is friendly and all students find that the small classes ensure that they receive individual help and advice from their tutors. The college is a member of CIFE, ARELS and FELCO. This means that teaching methods, facilities and so on are regularly inspected to ensure they reach the required high standard. The School of English is Recognised as Efficient by the British Council.

Basil Paterson's is non-residential, but the Accommodation Officer is pleased to arrange accommodation for all overseas students, with carefully chosen local families.

Courses For Overseas Students:

1. GCE 'O' and 'A' level or SCE 'O' and 'H' grade. Full range of subjects available. Advice given on choice of subjects for University entrance if required. Overseas students may enrol directly on these courses if English is their mother tongue or they have passed 'O' level/JMB English.

2. GCE or SCE Courses with English.

3. Introductory Courses in Maths, Science and Technical English.

4. Business Studies Courses.

5. Secretarial Courses: 4 weeks to one year.

6. English as a Foreign Language: All levels, all year round including summer. Short and long courses available.

Full details of all courses may be obtained from the above address. All prospective students and their parents are welcome to visit the college at any time, although they are advised to contact the college first to arrange an interview.

The Basil Paterson College, 22 Abercromby Place, Edinburgh EH3 6QE, Tel: 031-556 7695. Telex: 727815 BAPACO G.

BEECHLAWN TUTORIAL COLLEGE

Beechlawn is situated in the most attractive residential part of Oxford, about a mile from the city centre, and within easy reach of the university area, the river, museums and other places of interest. The house, surrounded by a lovely garden, stands on a quiet road where all the houses, designed by Seckham in the 1850s, are of architectural interest.

Young people have been taught at Beechlawn since the 1920s when university students came for individual coaching from Miss Janetta Keays Young, M.A., B.Litt., the founder of the present college. As years went by and particularly after World War II, when demand grew for tuition towards university entrance, many more pupils came to her and she developed Beechlawn into a tutorial college for girls. By the time she retired as Principal in 1966 it had become what it is today, Beechlawn Tutorial College, with 70-80 girls studying for the General Certificate of Education at Advanced Level.

Tuition is provided, in small groups or individually, by experienced graduate tutors and is suited to the abilities and needs of each pupil. All the normal subjects for GCE A and O level are taught. The college has its own laboratory for science subjects, photography dark-room, facilities for teaching Art, as well as a library and a good-sized common room. Field courses are organised for those taking Biology and Geography. Public examinations are taken at the college.

Advice about courses, careers and applications for higher education is given by a well-qualified Careers Counsellor. Many girls go on to universities, others to polytechnics, Art Colleges or further education and training. Beechlawn is very much concerned for the personal well-being of pupils as well as their academic progress.

Visits are organised to theatres and exhibitions in London or elsewhere, and pupils are encouraged to participate in cultural and recreational activities available in Oxford. Accommodation can be arranged with families living near and known to the college.

There will be an Open Day for visitors on Monday, 9th July 1984. Those wishing to come on another day should contact the college in advance.

The Principal will be glad to send further particulars on request.

Beechlawn Tutorial College,
1 Park Town,
Oxford OX2 6SN.
Telephone: 0865 57805.
Principal: Miss A. Brereton, M.A.

BOSWORTH
TUTORS

A small Tutorial College for only 60 students.

Fully residential for boys and girls from 15-18.

Specialists in G.C.E. O-Level tuition.

Specialists in G.C.E. A-Level tuition.

English language courses for overseas students.

Small classes (maximum 8) and individual tuition.

Separate supervised residences for boys and girls.

Friendly informal atmosphere in an adult environment.

Laboratories, Computer Centre, Sports facilities.

60 miles north of London. One hour on M1 motorway, or one hour by train.

Details from:

Admissions Registrar,
Bosworth Tutors,
9-11 St. George's Avenue,
Northampton NN2 6JA.
Telephone: (0604) 719988.

CAPITAL COLLEGE

WHAT MAKES A COLLEGE DIFFERENT?

Most students, parents and teachers would instantly mention the quality and commitment of the teaching staff. Once prospective teachers have undergone a thorough screening before appointment, the problem for adminstrators is how to maximise this. While worker participation is more familiar in industry, it can be restrained in education through set salary scales and the power head teachers like to keep to themselves.

The founders of CAPITAL COLLEGE set out from the start in 1980 to tackle the problem. They decided to have a college run by teachers, who would retain a teaching schedule. This remains so today. They decided that all educational decisions should be taken with the full agreement of those responsible for implementing them. This remains so today. They decided that all staff should be able to participate financially in the success of the college, in addition to salaries. This remains so today.

Although we cannot pretend to have found the ultimate, magical solution, we have tried to place teaching at the centre of college life and to encourage the wholehearted commitment of teachers.

Since we are wholly geared to helping students pass GCE 'O' & 'A' levels, our energies are closely focussed. We offer class tuition, regular testing and assignments, educational visits and films, effort prizes and aids to effective study/examination technique. We have a reading room, laboratory and cafeteria.

Aside from occasional advertisements, we have to rely upon our service to attract students. To date, generally one third of our students have studied with us for two years and another third have been recommended by our students. We hope this can be counted as an endorsement of our style. We also hope that this may encourage you to consider us and then decide.

Open days are held on Fridays throughout June and July and all are welcome to visit the college.

Capital College,
47 Red Lion Street,
London WC1R 4PF.
Tel: 01-404 5883.
Telex: 261426 ADFONE G.

CLYMPING COLLEGE

Clymping is a small residential/day College preparing up to 50 students for O and A level and vocational qualifications. Considerable emphasis is placed on realising academic potential to the full and the size of class varies from 5 to 12 depending upon the nature and level of work.

A balance is struck between the discipline of classes, supervised Prep and weekly examinations and a deliberately friendly, family-like environment with caring Staff and excellent food. The College has its own day Prep School on the campus and special Dyslexia therapy can be given to help those who may have learning problems. A full range of academic subjects and recreational activities is provided and we shall be pleased to send you our current prospectus.

The College is a member of the Conference for Independent Further Education.

For further information please contact: The Principals, C.R. Ibberson M.A., M.Inst.M., M.Inst.A.M., F.R.S.A., M.B.I.M. and A.Y. Ibberson, M.Inst.S.M., A.C.E.A., F.B.S.C., F.R.S.A., T.Cert.

Clymping College,
The Mill,
Clymping Street,
Clymping,
Littlehampton,
West Sussex BN17 5RN.
Telephone 09064 3710.

CONNAUGHT COLLEGE

Connaught College is a small tutorial college situated in the centre of the beautiful, historic City of Bath, which is one of the most visited tourist cities in the U.K. Founded in Roman times, the first King of England, Edgar was crowned here in 973, and the City reached its peak in the eighteenth century when it became a resort for the wealthy. Today, Bath, which is situated in the West of England, has splendid representations of its past in the form of Roman and Georgian architecture and is a colourful and picturesque holiday resort.

Since the Middle Ages, Bath has been a noted centre for education and the city now has a University, College of Higher Education and Art College.

Connaught College, founded in 1981, is housed in Westgate Buildings in the oldest part of Bath, opposite the mediaeval St. John's Hospital and near to the magnificent house of the Duke of Chandos. Westgate Buildings was mentioned by Jane Austen in her novel "Persuasion" and now provides comfortable premises for the College.

There are 120 students, studying for the General Certificate of Education, English language, business and law courses. About one-half of the students are British, the rest coming from up to 37 other countries. Apart from seven classrooms and administrative offices, there is a library, common room, cafeteria, listening centre and welfare office. Careers and University advice is given and tuition itself is provided either in small groups or on an individual basis, the philosophy of the College being to develop a person's education to produce a balanced and mature citizen, capable of thinking independently. Cramming is avoided.

The College has strong overseas links with twin cities in Europe and operates an exchange scheme. Culturally, there are thriving musical and dramatic societies and debating, social and other activities are often held. Trips to places of interest and to see plays are regularly organised and the College has a student Liaison Officer to organise events and sporting fixtures in collaboration with the Guild of Students whose officers are elected by the students.

Young people aged over fifteen are accepted for the College's courses and hostel or family accommodation can be arranged by the College's Accommodation Officer. Students can be met at airports or railway stations.

The College is headed by the Director under whom is the Principal and Vice-Principal and Senior Tutor who direct academic affairs. The Director and his staff are advised by a Board of Governors consisting of academics and local eminent people. The President is the Most Hon. The Marquess of Bath.

Visitors to the College are always welcome and it is helpful if an appointment is made with the College Secretary so that a programme can be devised and sufficient time made available to discuss the College with interested visitors.

Further information can be obtained from Mr. Davie, The Registrar's Department, Connaught College, Westgate Buildings, Bath, Avon, U.K. (Tel: 0225 63491. Telex: 449212 LANtel G UK.

DAVIES'S COLLEGE, HOVE

Staff

There are approximately 70 members of the teaching staff comprising 40 full-time Staff Tutors and 30 part-time Private Tuition Staff.

Methods of Teaching

Our teaching philisophy follows closely that found in Universities in the U.K. Lectures and tutorials are followed by individual sessions with tutors, and our aim is to devise a combination which enables each Student to make the very most of his/her ability.

Academic Reports

Five reports are issued automatically direct to Parents or Guardians in each academic year. Additional reports and consultations are available at any time on request.

Locality and Transport

The College occupies five spacious buildings in a pleasant residential area in Hove, a seaside town adjacent to Brighton, offering excellent facilities for Students in the way of study and leisure. London is one hour away by train.

Principal: R. Bellerby, M.A., B.Sc., Grad Cert Ed, F.B.I.S., F.B.I.M.
Davies's College,
44 Cromwell Road,
Hove,
East Sussex BN3 3ER.
Tel: Brighton (0273) 723911.
Telex: 877810 DAVCOL G.

Open Day: Tuesday June 12th 1984. Visitors most welcome at other times by appointment.

DAVIES'S COLLEGE, LONDON

Staff

Altogether there are about 130 members of the teaching staff, comprising 60 full-time Group Tutors and some 70 full-time and part-time Private Tutors.

Methods of Teaching

The Students are taught by various methods, all of which differ significantly from the methods used in schools. When Students first approach Davies's, advice is given on the most appropriate choice of subjects and teaching methods according to each individual Student's aims and ability. The majority are taught by the Group method, which has been designed to ensure that every Student receives individual attention without loss of contact with other Students. Private lessons are also available.

Reports

Parents and Guardians may obtain reports on the work and conduct of Students at any time on request.

Locality and Transport

Davies's occupies a large building in Holborn, which is a pleasant district in Central London. The nearest Underground Station which is 3 minutes walk from Davies's is Holborn (Kingsway). Heathrow and Gatwick airports are easily accessible by train.

Open Day: Tuesday October 9th 1984. Visitors most welcome at other times by appointment.

Principal: J.L. Norden, M.A. (Cambridge), A.C.I.E., F.B.I.M. Davies's College, 66 Southampton Row, London WC18 4BY. Tel: 01-405 2933. Telex: 28604 (ref. 3468) MONREF G.

THE EDINBURGH TUTORIAL COLLEGE

AND
AMERICAN SCHOOL OF EDINBURGH

Principal: A.W. Morris, B.Sc, M.Inst P.

We are the only Scottish college running a British and American educational programme at pre-university level. The Edinburgh Tutorial College and the American School of Edinburgh, founded in 1973, are sister organisations and are located in an elegant Georgian terrace with a pleasant view across the lawns and trees to St. Mary's Cathedral. We are situated right in the very heart of the city, in the fashionable West End area of the famous New Town. Edinburgh itself is justly famous for its noble architecture, its lively culture and its many historical connections. It has all the advantages of a capital city — but none of the pressures. Edinburgh people are renowned for their friendly hospitality and always seem to find time to welcome their guests.

The Edinburgh Tutorial College offers full and part time courses for all GCE 'O/A' level and SCE 'O/H' grade examinations, as well as EFL-based courses for foreign students preparing for entry to institutes of higher education. During the summer months, the College runs a series of highly popular English Language courses, which form part of an exciting social and cultural programme. All members of staff are fully-qualified graduates, and have been carefully chosen not only for their teaching ability and experience, but also for their interest in and commitment to the education of young people. The classrooms are light and spacious and are well equipped with the most modern teaching aids. There are extensive laboratory, darkroom, library and computer facilities, as well as a comfortable student common room.

During the summer, the American School of Edinburgh will run a 1984 Heritage course, designed especially for American visitors to Scotland with an interest in Scottish history and culture. The programme will include lectures and guided tours, taking in the familiar and the less familiar — a golden opportunity, in short, for Americans of Scottish origin to explore their roots. During the academic year the American School provides an independent co-educational curriculum for 7th to 12th Grade students who wish to continue with their studies in an educational system with which they are familiar. The School is also a testing centre for all major US testing programmes.

The Accommodation Secretary will be pleased to arrange accommodation either in hotels or with selected Edinburgh families on a full or half board basis.

For prospectus and full details of tuition fees and accommodation, please contact:

The Principal,
29 Chester Street,
Edinburgh EH3 7EN.
Tel: 031-225 9888.

GREYLANDS INTERNATIONAL COLLEGE

**Independent Residential College of Further Education.
Incorporating Mallinsons International School (1922)
of Photography, Film and Video.
. . . The one for you!**

An established form of education presented with a modern approach including:

★ GCE 'O' and 'A' level courses in most subjects;
★ outstanding tutorial qualifications and very small classes;
★ flying qualifications to Private Pilots Licence;
★ modern language and science laboratories;
★ hovercraft commander's licence;
★ sailing, water-skiing, wind-surfing and swimming;
★ archery, basketball, football and physical education, etc.;
★ photographic school with lavish equipment and studios, including audio-visual and video. Courses for 'O' and 'A' level photography: the Licentiate of the Royal Photography, Film and Video Professional Diploma;
★ examination boards include University of London — Associated Examining Board — Cambridge University — Royal Society of Arts — Pitmans Examinations Institute — London Chamber of Commerce and Industry — Joint Matriculation Board;
★ extensive computer training facilities for GCE, etc.;
★ A.B.A.C. (Association of Business and Administrative Computing) taught;
★ BEC General and National taught;
★ open 365 days per year. Residential, co-educational;
★ class maximum 12 pupils;
★ detailed university entrance preparation and career counselling.

Situated in beautiful grounds on the beach at Bembridge in the Isle of Wight.

Members of the European Council of International Schools: the British Association of Commercial and Industrial Education and the Association of Tutors Incorporated.

For further information please contact: Greylands International College, Bembridge, Isle of Wight. Telephone (0983) 872871/872847/874361

HARROGATE TUTORIAL COLLEGE

Department of English as a Foreign Language recognised as efficient by The British Council

The Harrogate Tutorial College and its sister college in Leeds, Pennine Independent College, both opened in September 1981. Harrogate is less than three hours by rail from London and close to Leeds and Bradford, and Manchester Airports.

Our highly experienced teachers specialise in building student confidence and teaching examination techniques to either small groups of students or individuals.

Overseas students stay initially with families close to the College. All families are vetted by the college and students have their own rooms and meals provided. We consider it essential for oversas students understanding and command of English that practice is continuous and that they feel part of an English family. Assistance is also given to students with find houses and flats in the area.

The Student Welfare Officer has wide experience in dealing with the problems and difficulties students may encounter and is in close communication with the host families. She is responsible for all pastoral matters and organises a series of cultural visits and recreational activities.

The colleges offer a wide range of courses, ranging from one year intensive GCE Courses to introductory English as a Foreign Language, English for Special Purposes and the Summer School, Holidays in English. The small classes ensure the most rapid student progress and good student-teacher rapport. Careers guidance and help with College and University entrance is given automatically.

The most recent course developments are the Harrogate Executive Language Programmes which are balanced, highly intensive, English Language programmes tailored for the individual.

G.C.E. Department

'O' and 'A' Levels & Retakes, Full and Part-time, 6 month — 2 year Courses. Intensive Revision Courses. Examination Centre.

English For Overseas Students

Intensive Courses for:- Cambridge Preliminary, Lower, Intermediate and Proficiency Certificates. R.S.A. and J.M.B. English. R.S.A. (Teaching) T.E.F.L. Diploma. *Holidays in English, International.* Residential Language and Culture Courses. Full programmes of Sports, Visits and Activities.

School Of Business & Computer Studies

Basic Secretarial Skills. Multilingual and Advanced Courses. Modern Office Technology. Word Processing, Computing and Programming, Practical Experience. Examination Centre.

The colleges do not have open days but the Principal or a senior member of staff are always available to answer queries and classes are open to visitors. For further information please contact: The Principal, Harrogate Tutorial College, 1 Station Square, Harrogate HG1 1SY. Tel: (0423) 501041, 58341. Telex: Mysec 57453 G.

INTERNATIONAL TUTORIAL COLLEGE, EXETER

Exeter is situated in the heart of the south west of England, a region renowned for its natural beauty. The International Tutorial College and International School of English occupy attractive buildings set in their own beautiful gardens and were both founded by the present Principal, Mrs D. M. Bryant.

The International Tutorial College specialises in GCE General Certificate of Education, Ordinary and Advanced level studies, for students who intend to go on to Higher Education in the United Kingdom, and wish to enter a University or Polytechnic. University entrance normally requires 5 'O' level and 2 'A' level passes. English language is a compulsory subject. Many overseas qualifications are accepted as equivalent to General Certificate of Education passes at 'O' level, and the college can advise on these matters.

Subjects offered at 'O' level (one year course):
English, Mathematics, Additional Mathematics, Physics, Chemistry, Biology, Accounts, Technical Drawing, Business Studies, Commerce, Computer Programming.

Subjects offered at 'A' level (one/two year course):
English, Mathematics, Further Mathematics, Physics, Chemistry, Economics, Accounts, Biology, Business Studies, Computer Programming, Law.

Laboratory facilities are available for students taking Computer Studies, Physics, Chemistry and Biology. Teaching is in small groups averaging 6-8 students. Reports are issued monthly. Courses begin early September or January each year.

The International School

The International School, a founder member of A.R.E.L.S. is the largest and longest-established school of English in the South West and is situated on an attractive campus near city centre. It has small classes at all levels, language laboratories, a library and video facility, school cafeteria and social centre for indoor sports/leisure facilities. Full social programme is offered with all courses.

Intensive English Language courses throughout the year and preparation for all major English exams, in particular for Cambridge First Certificate and Proficiency. Total immersion mini group courses for adults (maximum 5 students per class). Summer vacation courses for adults (16+), and juniors (11-14) — 3/4 week courses July and August.

Accommodation arranged by the School with carefully selected English families.

You are welcome to visit Exeter and see the school and the college in operation. Please contact the Principal, The International Tutorial College, 44/46 Magdalen Road, Exeter, Devon EX2 4TE. Tel: (0392) 73781/50096. Telex: 42931 INTEX G.

IRWIN ACADEMY

Irwin Academy is an Independent co-educational college of further education providing tuition in a wide range of subjects for the G.C.E. examinations at Ordinary and Advanced levels. Founded in 1975, it has expanded to its present maximum enrolment of 75 students.

The emphasis is on hard work, close supervision and personal attention. The average class size is six. Each student is interviewed formally by the Principal twice each term to check on progress. There are termly examinations, the results of which are sent to parents. The Director is responsible for advising students about applications to institutions of higher education. The teaching is in the hands of over thirty tutors, each of whom is a graduate. Private study during the day takes place under the supervision of a member of the staff. Assignments are set for the vacation period.

The main buildings are three adjoining late Victorian houses, ten minutes' walk from the railway station and city centre. Opposite the Academy is a large park, with facilities for sport. The University of Leicester buildings face the same park. The buildings contain the tutorial and private study rooms, the laboratory area and the rooms for Art and Technical Drawing classes.

Although most students are boarders, some live in self-catering accommodation, and some make their own arrangements.

Rules are kept to the minimum: co-operation, conscientiousness and courtesy are the key-words. There is no uniform and no student has authority over another. Facilities for most sports are available, but participation is not compulsory. There are no punishments, but any student who obviously is not prepared to work and be responsible may expect to be asked to leave — the aim of the establishment is to provide an atmosphere conducive to the success of every student who is mature enough to thrive in such an atmosphere.

A prospectus and an introductory cassette are available from the Secretary, Mrs. V. Thorpe, Irwin Academy, 164 London Road, Leicester LE2 1ND. Telephone Leicester (0533) 552648. Appointments to discuss educational matters and to look around the Academy may be made throughout the year.

Director: D. J. Williams, B.A. Hons. (Q.U.B.), Cert, Ed. Principal: H. Sezer, B.Sc. (Hons.), M.A., Dip. Econ. Dev.

THE MILESTONE SCHOOLS

The Milestone Schools are a well established group of three schools each with a separate identity. **The Preparatory School,** in New Bond Street, coaches boys and girls from the age of 9 to 13 in readiness for the Common Entrance Examination and admission to the Public Schools. It has its own Headmaster whose rich experience in preparing children of this age group has led to an enviable reputation in the placement of boys and girls in well known major public schools. The Middle School and Senior Tutorial Department are in the heart of South Kensington, an area which contains a large number of famous tutorial schools. **The Middle School** offers a two year course to GCE 'O' level for boys and girls in the age range 13½ to 16. The prevailing attitude is one of realistic hard work. For the first year, the curriculum is broad-based. At the beginning of the second year, each student is carefully advised on the choice of his GCE 'O' level subjects. Throughout both years, there are current affairs discussion periods and a games afternoon. **The Senior Tutorial Department** specializes in the further education of students over the age of 16. Some will be preparing their 'A' levels at the Milestone instead of remaining at school in a more traditional VI form. Others will be re-taking 'A' level examinations in which they have not obtained the grades necessary for university entrance. Yet others will be studying for admission to Oxford and Cambridge. Tuition in a full range of subjects is offered in small groups of not more than eight. Science subjects are taught in three well equipped laboratories, whilst the teaching of arts subjects follows the pattern of the university tutorial. A sense of purpose and hard work couples with a relaxed and happy atmosphere conducive to academic success. The Principal discusses with each student personally the completion of the standard form of application for admission to British Universities, (UCCA). The choice of University and Polytechnic places is extremely important and careful attention is given to helping the student reach the right decisions. All tutors are university graduates and play an active part in the academic community. London's vast resources, in terms of galleries, museums and theatres, are constantly tapped and the Principal and tutors together work to ensure that each student reaches the upper limits of his potential.

The school's own prospectus and registration form are obtainable on application to the school secretary.

The Milestone Schools
85 Cromwell Road,
London SW7.
Tel: 373 4956/7. Telex: Milest 291987.

NORTH MIDLANDS COLLEGE

The college was founded by a small educational company in 1982 after much experience in the field. It is the only tutorial college in the area and it caters for all aspects of O and A level courses as well as a wide variety of interest courses available to the public, especially computing and languages. Teaching is on site and there are common room facilities for students.

Teaching is available on a group and/or individual basis, with class sizes never exceeding four students. The permanent staff is experienced with all tutors teaching the subject in which they graduated. The vast majority are also qualfied teachers. Flexibility of courses allows close tailoring to meet individual needs. Virtually any combination of O and A level subjects is available, although the college does not teach Nuffield Sciences. A level courses are offered over two years or lesser periods and resit candidates are accepted for either one year or a shorter time if it is felt that the student can do himself justice. There is no age limit for enrolment. Field courses in Geography and Biology are run each Easter holiday and are open to interested parties outside the college. Students from abroad, particularly America, may be accepted for a Liberal Studies course which may or may not be examination orientated.

College also runs courses in English as a Foreign Language. Year courses (class sizes 6-10) commence in September each year for those with elementary and intermediate skills in English, leading to JMB O level English for Foreigners (recognised as a university entrance qualification). Eight week summer schools aim at students with a good basis in the language and courses are also available in Commercial English for businessmen. All courses also lead to a College Diploma.

Accommodation and welfare are in the hands of a full time accommodation officer who regularly inspects all lodgings and acts in loco parentis in welfare matters. Generally accommodation is with a family but college also offers a number of small self catering houses for those who can organise themselves sufficiently. Medical care is arranged through a local medical practice.

Beaumont Secretarial College, a sister college, runs full time courses for the training of personal secretaries. The classes have twelve students maximum and utilise very up to date equipment. Typing is taught on electronic typewriters and word processing is a standard part of the course. It is possible to combine a secretarial course with academic subjects if required.

For further details please contact:

The Principal,
North Midlands College,
6 Jasper Street,
Hanley,
Stoke on Trent ST1 3DA.
Telephone (0782) 260971.

THE OXFORD ACADEMY

Director: Mrs S.M. Mason M.H.C.I.M.A.

Founded 30 years ago, the Academy is a residential school offering a range of courses and good accommodation to students from all over the world. The school, with its 5 residential houses, is situated in an attractive suburb, about 15 minutes walk from the centre of Oxford and is well-known for its high academic standards and friendly atmosphere. The facilities of the Academy (including library, listening centre, video room) and the full social programme are open to all students who choose from:

★ General English as a Foreign Language (EFL) in classes

★ Individual tuition in EFL

★ English for Special Purposes

★ G.C.E. courses ('O' & 'A' Levels)

★ Special courses (eg. English Literature) on request.

Prospectus and further details from:

The Secretary,
The Oxford Academy,
18 Bardwell Rd, Oxford OX2 6SP.
Telephone: Oxford 512174.
Telex: 83147 OXACAD.

PADWORTH COLLEGE

Padworth is an international, residential sixth form college for girls aged fifteen plus. It was founded in 1963, one of the first of its kind, with the belief that many girls in their middle teens require a rather different environment than that offered by more traditional schools if they are to develop their intellects and personalities in a way that will equip them for modern life. The aim is to combine small classes in a wide range of liberal arts and science subjects with a young adult atmosphere. Business studies (for Business Education Council Examinations), and Secretarial Studies, are also available (the latter full or part-time). There is a sizeable English as a Foreign Language department. Overseas students are accepted at all levels of language competence for full-time English language courses. These students enjoy the advantage of living with a student body which is 80% English speaking. The English department also supplies advanced level courses for 'A' level students (studying Maths, Statistics and the Sciences for example) whose English is not perfect. Summer and Easter holiday English courses are also available.

Though academic study is central, the social life of the College is organised to cater for many interests. There are regular visits to theatres, and cultural excursions. Facilities exist in the grounds for tennis, swimming (in the summer), horse-riding, basket and volley ball, and other games can be played at nearby sports centres. Great emphasis is placed on the happiness and welfare of the students. Social units are small and a large proportion of the staff live in.

Padworth House and the Church nearby have existed since the 11th century. The present house is an eighteenth century manor house incorporating an older Tudor house. It was occupied by the same family from the eightenth century to the 1930s. Features of the interior are the hall and drawing-room. A special Heritage Open Day will be held on Friday, July 6th, when visitors will be given a tour of the house, a talk on the upstairs and downstairs life of this typical country mansion, and the opportunity to see the English language Summer School for boys and girls in full swing. Tea will be served. For those interested in the academic year courses, interviews with the Principal can be arranged. Group visits to the College can be made by arrangement on other dates.

For further information please contact:

Mrs Munden,
Padworth College,
near Reading,
Berkshire RG7 4NP.
Telephone: (073 529) 2644/5
Telex via 847423 COC-RG-G Prefix 'For Padworth College'

ST ALDATE'S COLLEGE OXFORD

St. Aldates College is the largest independent GCE College of its kind in Oxford and its small-classes teaching policy is designed to provide personal assistance to bring students to a high grade 'A' Level standard.

The College offers 2 year (6 term) and one year (3 term) concentrated courses covering 3 subjects at 'A' Level. Specialist 1, 2 and 3 term "Retake" Courses are also provided with the emphasis on intensive syllabus cover, past examination questions and 'Mocks'. GCE 'O' Level courses are also available.

St. Aldates College also offers Summer Courses at Oxford to USA University students. The courses lead to Certificates giving 'Degree Credits'.

St. Aldates has adopted the modern educational approach that GCE subjects, especially at 'A' Level, should be chosen on the basis of the profession that students intend making their life's work. Thus, when the career objective is known, students are steered towards the study of subjects that will be of most assistance when preparing for their professional qualifying examinations or University and Polytechnic Degrees.

As a natural development of its 'objective' teaching policy, the College now offers a one year (3 term) Business Studies course covering the M.A.B.E. (Association of Business Executives) Examination. The syllabus comprises Economics of Industry and Business, Accounting & Finance, Commercial (Business) Law, Business Administration, Marketing, Computing and other essential subjects for those planning for executive level appointments.

St. Aldates College is a Member of the Conference for Independent Further Education (C.I.F.E.), Member of the Independent Schools Information Service the Association for the Recognition of Business Schools (A.R.B.S.) and an official GCE Examining Centre. It is co-educational, multi-cultural and provides excellent living accommodation in its own flatlets and rooms or within selected Oxford families.

A limited number of open scholarships are granted.

Fully explanatory Prospectuses are available on request in writing or telephone Oxford (8065) 240111. Prospective students should state whether the College 'GCE' or 'BUSINESS STUDIES' Prospectus is desired.

St. Aldates College, (Dept.4GB),
Rose Place,
Oxford,
England.

ST. GILES COLLEGE

Principal: J.H. BRADFORD
A member of CIFE. Co-Educational, 16+. Annual intake 50 — 60 students

St. Giles College, Eastbourne is one of four Colleges in the St. Giles group founded by Mr. Paul Lindsay in 1955. The others are in London, Brighton and San Francisco. All the colleges are concerned with teaching English, the Eastbourne college concentrating on GCE 'O' and 'A' level courses and University preparation.

Eastbourne is a famous English seaside resort with a population of some 70,000 and is 100km from London. It enjoys one of the best climates in the United Kingdom, being sheltered by the South Downs and offers plenty in the way of cultural and sporting facilities.

The College is set in its own grounds with good facilities and a large garden and is some 200m from the seafront and about 2km from the town centre. There are two well-equipped science laboratories, a library and private study room, also a large cafeteria and student lounge. There is a college minibus which operates a free service to and from the town centre daily.

The annual intake is restricted to 80 students — both British and overseas. The Principal ensures that the teaching reflects the St. Giles commitment to the Counselling approach to education. Briefly this ensures that the students are responsible to a large extent for their own learning pace.

At St. Giles we believe in creating an adult learning environment with as few rules as possible and giving scope for all students to develop at their own rate. One lesson each week in each subject on the timetable is reserved for a counselling period with the teacher.

Students are helped with application to University in the UK or USA. Since some students find that their English is inadequate, we have a teacher with resonsibility for remedial English classes; these can be fitted into the student's GCE timetable.

St. Giles is a day college and our students are accommodated with families in Eastbourne. They may choose from two possible types of accommodation: as a paying guest in a private family or in a larger hostel-type residence.

Visitors are always welcome to the College and the Principal will be pleased to give help and advice to students and parents.

St. Giles College,
13 Silverdale Road,
Eastbourne,
East Sussex BN20 7AJ.
Telephone: 0323 29167.

ST. JOSEPH'S HALL

St. Joseph's Hall

The Manor House

St. Joseph's Hall is situated in Oxford, the city of dreaming spires and seat of the oldest university in Britain. With its superb medieval architecture and tradition of scholarship, Oxford provides as ideal a setting for a study holiday as for a longer academic course.

St. Joseph's is an independent institution of further and higher education. It is fully equipped with the most modern teaching aids, and other special facilities. The College offers high quality educational and academic courses for overseas and British students. Accommodation is arranged either in the College's own residence, The Manor House or with English host families. The College is divided into three departments:

The Further Education Department provides GCE Ordinary and Advanced level courses for British and Overseas Students of 3-4 or 9 months duration (Sept/June), which prepare students for the qualifications needed for entry into UK and North American universities.

The EFL (English as a Foreign Language) department, recognised as efficient by The British Council, provides short intensive summer holiday courses combining a holiday in one of Europe's loveliest cities with study of the English language and long-term academic courses leading to recognised EFL examinations. It also organises special courses for various groups of professionals tailored to their particular needs.

The Computing Department runs a range of courses: holiday Computing courses, which can be combined with EFL courses, courses which lead to public examinations, and other courses, including computer programming, word processing and introductory courses for businessmen. The computer used for these courses is of the Government approved standard for education in Britain.

Cultural/Educational Tours. In association with Transun Travel, an experienced youth travel operator, we can arrange a customised educational, cultural and holiday visit to the UK, Europe and Worldwide. Taking advantage of Oxford's unique position, we arrange courses in conjunction with eminent academics, and arrange related cultural tours having the hallmark of quality combined with flexibility. We are thus able to advise on both the academic and the cultural aspects of your visit, and make the necessary arrangements, tailoring the tour to suit particular needs, (eg for North American High School and University groups).

All enquiries to:

St. Joseph's Hall,
Marketing Dept.,
Junction Rd.,
Oxford OX4 2UJ.
Tel: (0865) 711829; Telex: 83635.

ST. MATTHEWS TUTORIAL COLLEGE

Registrar: E.V. Newcombe-Jones, B.Sc., Dip. Ed.
Director of Studies: P.H. Brooks, B.A., Cert.Ed., F.R.G.S.

St. Matthews is a well established and successful Tutorial College situated in the University City of Oxford, one of the most pleasant cities in the world to live, work or study. The College is concerned mainly with preparing British and foreign students for the G.C.E. examinations at Ordinary and Advanced Levels and most of our students proceed to University or Polytechnics.

St. Matthews also organises holiday E.F.L. courses for overseas students. These courses are held during the Easter and Summer Vacations. English as a Foreign Language is taught to beginners, intermediate and advanced students and if required special tuition in Scientific or Business English can be arranged. In addition overseas students can decide to join for one or more terms of study in order to prepare for the Cambridge Certificate and J.M.B. Examination in English.

The method of teaching is based directly on the tutorial system of the Oxford Colleges. Students are taught through individual tuition or in small study groups. The aim of the College is to provide tuition of the highest possible standard and by close personal supervision to encourage and motivate students to attain their full academic potential.

The College Tutorial staff are men and women of the highest calibre. Many are graduates of Oxford University. Our E.F.L. teachers are invariably experienced in this field and students make rapid progress.

Courses are fully residential and students may lodge either in one of the college hostels or with a local family. Accommodation is conveniently situated near to the St Matthews Study Centre.

The college issues Prospectuses outlining the G.C.E. and E.F.L. courses together with details of accommodation and fees etc. Prospectus and application forms may be obtained from The Registrar. (Please write or telephone).

Upon receipt of completed enrolment forms and deposit on tuition fees, overseas students can if necessary be forwarded a Certificate of Studentship which will assist with entry formalities. The College is registered with the British Home Office. If required the College can arrange for overseas students to be met at Heathrow Airport.

For further details please contact:

The Registrar,
St Matthews Tutorial College,
52 St Giles,
Oxford OX1 3LU.
Tel: Oxford (0865) 53192.

STAKE FARM COLLEGE

Principals: Miss J.E. Norwood-Jefferson, B.A.
Miss E.M. Heaton, B.A.

Stake Farm College is an International College for girls of 16 and over. It was established originally in 1953 as a Finishing School for English and foreign girls. Today it still retains many of its orignial features but has introduced others more relevant to the modern world. The international background is still the most important feature. English speaking girls follow courses leading to G.C.E. O and A level examinations and foreign girls follow courses in English language leading to a variety of E.F.L. (English as a Foreign Language) examinations at all levels.

In addition all students follow a general "finishing" course which includes a wide variety of optional studies, and which encourages a truly international atmosphere as all students can work together in study groups where language differences are not a handicap, and in which the variety of cultural backgrounds contribute to an enriching experience for all students.

Main courses are selected which will lead to the appropriate examination required for a future career. These subjects are taught in small tutorial groups, sometimes even individually, by well qualified and experienced tutors. Subjects available are English Language and Literature, Maths, History, Geography, Economics, French, German, Spanish, Italian, Latin, Biology, Art and History of Art. In addition all students study a selection of Finishing subjects from the following: Business Studies, Home Management, Health and Beauty, Personal Presentation, Arts and Crafts, Drama, Music and Dancing, Computer Studies.

The College has its own squash court, tennis court, and facilities for badminton, volley ball and table tennis. Swimming is available at a near-by indoor swimming pool all the year and in a heated open-air pool in the summer. Riding is available at several local riding stables. Coaching can be arranged in most sports at an extra charge.

Excursions are arranged to the many stately homes and gardens in the South of England and to local places of interest. Visits to London and to Museums, Art Galleries, Exhibitions and Historic Buildings are organised during each term and each afternoon during the Summer School.

Accommodation is mainly in the College itself. Bedrooms are for two or three girls. Some girls may be boarded out with approved families. Foreign girls often prefer this arrangement as the close contact with an English family provides additional opportunities for practising their English.

Prospectus and Summer School Prospectus available from:
The Secretary,
Stake Farm College,
Sevenoaks,
Kent TN15 0JU.
Visitors are welcomed by appointment.

SYMONDSBURY COLLEGE

Symondsbury College offers a pleasant alternative to the conventional learning situation, and one in which students are better able to realise their full academic potential and achieve higher exam successes.

The College aims primarily to prepare students for entrance to university. We also prepare students for any career requiring ordinary or advanced level passes in G.C.E. examinations and we provide tuition in most subjects.

Throughout the years we have established a very high reputation with parents, schools and colleges for providing an exceptional standard of examination coaching and for flexibility in matching courses to the individual requirement of students. To this end, every student is taught as a *separate individual* at all times and has the careful and undivided attention of his tutor in each subject.

We are at all times concerned that the school's numbers be limited to the number of students that we feel we can keep in close contact with throughout their stay with us. With only fifty full-time students we are able to enjoy an inter-dependent community with a free flow of ideas between staff and students. In this way we are able to preserve the valuable 'family' type of community feeling.

Members of staff are always accessible throughout the working day for problems of any nature.

On the premises, apart from a large number of tutorial rooms and the normal facilities, we have three well-equipped laboratories, an examination room for regular mock exams and a constantly supervised prep-room.

The strength of our College lies both in our emphasis on individual tuition and the exceptionally high calibre of our tutors. We have a large and excellent graduate staff with a wide range of experience and interests, all teaching their own specialist subjects.

The College stands in its own grounds of three acres in the village of Symondsbury which, together with the surrounding countryside and coast has been designated as an area of outstanding natural beauty. The shops and ameneties of Bridport are less than one mile away. There is regular coach service to London from Bridport and trains run hourly from Dorchester to Waterloo.

Summer Courses

For students from outside the U.K. the College offers residential courses in various subjects including English Culture, English History, Fine Art and English Language. For details of these, please apply for our Summer Course brochure.

For a prospectus on G.C.E. and pre-University courses, please apply to:

The Secretary,
Symondsbury College,
Symondsbury,
Bridport,
Dorset DT6 6HD.
Tel. 0308 56288.

UNIVERSITY TUTORIAL COLLEGE

University Tutorial College founded in 1889 is one of the oldest-established Colleges of independent further education in the United Kingdom. For almost one hundred years we have prepared students from all over the world for successful and fulfilling careers. Though the building is traditional our facilties are recognised as being some of the most modern of any tutorial establishment in London.

Our close links with the universities and professional institutions enables us to offer a teaching programme combining the best of university methods of instruction and those of any school. As an examination centre for The London University students are required to sit their General Certificate of Education examinations, (O & A Levels), on the college premises. In the Business Studies and Secretarial courses we have similar arrangements with the professional examining bodies.

Our extensive record of high achievement is due to our excellent teaching standards and ensures that students have a good start to their future careers.

Facilities

All in a modern working environment include: Well equipped laboratories, newly-built Lecture Theatre, Library, Refectory.

Location

The College is situated in Central London, close to The British Musuem and London University.

Courses

One year full-time G.C.E. 'O' & 'A' Levels
Three year Law Degree.
I.A.M. & A.B.E. Business Studies Diplomas
Intensive one-term secretarial courses.

Tuition

Classroom teaching with seminars and tutorials. At UTC we recognise the need for personal attention including allocating specific times for students to discuss progress, problems, and other academic matters.

For further details write or visit us in London at:

University Tutorial College,
103 Great Russell Street,
London W.C.1B 3LA,
United Kingdom.
Tel: 01-580 4676.
Telex: 28554 LANGSC.G.

We will be happy to show you round the College.

WESSEX TUTORS

Wessex Tutors is a college in the centre of Winchester which provides tuition for about 50 students in GCE 'O' and 'A' level exams and Oxbridge entry exams. Tuition takes place in our buildings in Parchment Street, where the facilities include three Science Laboratories, an Art room and a Computer room.

Winchester is one of England's oldest Cathedral cities, and is the ancient capital of the country. It has been a cultural centre and tourist attraction for centuries. Set in the heart of Hampshire, it is an hour from London and Oxford by train, and is within easy reach of Southampton and Heathrow airports. Winchester, with a population of 50,000, has theatres and cinemas, and a wide range of sporting facilities.

Tuition

The main strength of the college lies in the high calibre of the graduate teaching staff. Tuition is on an individual basis, or in very small groups. This enables us to teach students at their own pace and to prepare them to take exams as soon as they are ready to do so. 'A' level courses take between one and two years, and intensive three month re-take courses are also available. Any combination of subjects is possible: 'O' levels can be combined with 'A' levels; English tuition can be combined with GCE subjects, and general Computer courses with any subjects studied.

English for Overseas Students

Students are prepared either individually, or in small groups for the following exams: Cambridge Proficiency, R.S.A., J.M.B., the British/Swiss Chamber of Commerce exams, and T.O.E.F.L.

Tuition in English can be combined with tuition in G.C.E. subjects, and the balance between the two can be altered as the student's English improves. Intensive language courses are held during the summer in preparation for enrolment in University courses or G.C.E. courses in the Autumn. Short specialist courses are held regularly throughout the year for overseas undergraduates in English literature, technical and scientific English and computing.

Further Education and Careers Advice

Students are given advice about applying to British and American Universities and Polytechnics. S.A.T. tests can be arranged and help is given with the choice of University and the completion of application forms.

Accommodation

Accommodation is arranged with selection local families or in self-catering flats.

The Principal will be pleased to see prospective parents at any time. For prospectuses, please write to: Mrs. E. Backhouse, M.A.Cantab., 14 Parchment Street, Winchester, Hampshire. Tel: (0962 53964).

WINCHESTER TUTORIAL COLLEGE

Student Hostel

Student Study Room

A tradition of over twenty years of first class Individual Tuition for all O and A level subjects.
All tuition and study takes place on the premises.
Three laboratories, supervised study room, computing and music.
Summer English Language courses.
Carefully chosen graduate staff.
We have our own hostel or can arrange accommodation with selected local families.
Examination Centre for Cambridge, J.M.B., London, Oxford and Oxford & Cambridge Boards.

For further information, please contact:
The Principal,
Winchester Tutorial College,
18 St Thomas's Street,
Winchester,
Hants.
Telephone: 0962 68793.

WOLSEY HALL TUTORIAL COLLEGE

For nearly a century Wolsey Hall has been the foremost college in the field of distance learning and has provided courses for GCE 'O' and 'A' levels and London University external degrees. The college has strong links overseas and there are students of Wolsey Hall in almost every country of the world.

In recent years seminars and face-to-face tuition has formed a growing part of the College's teaching. A natural and logical development was the establishment of a full tutorial college and Law School.

Individual Tutorial approach

The college caters for those students who wish to receive private tuition coupled with a high level of personal supervision. The college has as its first aim the creation of confidence, involvement and motivation and seeks to build these qualities by close personal contact between tutor and student and by constant personal counselling.

In common with the Universities of Oxford and Cambridge the college has adopted the individual tutorial as the core of its teaching system and uses both seminars and lectures in support. All tutors are graduates and many have higher degrees. The Tutorial College Principal, Mr David Watson, MA (Oxon), is a teacher of considerable ability and experience.

The College is housed in a fine Victorian building in its own grounds just ten minutes walk from the centre of Oxford. The central administration, library, seminar rooms, common room, video and computer facility are all in the main building. Science laboratories and art studios are situated close by.

Courses

Most students will be preparing for GCE at 'A' level or for the University of London LL.B. degree. A group will also be prepared for the entrance examinations to Oxford and Cambridge Universities.

From 1984 the college will offer courses for American students wishing to study abroad. There are a variety of courses from summer programmes to a full year of study in Oxford. Credits and advanced placement may be obtained and interviews can be arranged with colleges in the University for suitably qualified candidates.

For full details of courses please write to:

The Registrar, Dept W2A,
Wolsey Hall Tutorial College,
66 Banbury Road,
Oxford OX2 6PR.

Tel: 0865 511187/8 (24 hours)

WOODHILL

Situation: 2½ miles from Bungay, 4 miles from Beccles on the Norfolk, Suffolk Border. Age range 14-18. Fees £1,500 per term.

Woodhill is a small residential Tutorial College where above all else we strive for excellence and, if a great deal of personal attention can make the difference between a student passing and failing the G.C.E. exams, we will provide it. The school is part of a specially designated preservation area in the middle of the beautiful Waveney Valley and is housed in a Georgian Rectory overlooking the river. The five acres of grounds are mostly laid out as lawns and the students are encouraged to use them as much as possible for football and other sporting activities.

Most of the students live in the main building with the girls in their own wing. The bedroom accommodation is comfortable with students sharing two, three or four to a room. Downstairs there is a T.V. room, Dining room, and a couple of large study rooms where silence is obligatory. The purpose built class room block is about fifty yards from the main building across the basket ball pitch.

However pleasant the buildings and situation may be the primary objective of the school is to get Students through their G.C.E. exams. We achieve this by only employing experienced teachers and keeping classes as small as possible. Without doubt, the education is intensive and it is our intention to push our students to their limits. The speed of teaching is about one and a half times that of an orthodox school and there are exam level tests in each subject three or four times per term. The results of these tests are taken seriously as they give an excellent measure of a student's progress and remedial action is taken if things begin to go wrong.

While there is no entrance exam for Woodhill, the school is academically biased and is specifically geared to getting students through their G.C.E. exams. We take pride in our pass rate and feel that a great deal of personal interest in each student is the secret of success.

For further information please contact:

The Principal,
Woodhill,
Ellingham,
Bungay,
Suffolk NR35 2EP.
Telephone: (0508 42) 202.

Independent Boarding Schools

School	Type	Ages	Exam	No.	Region	Page
Nevill Holt	B	7-13	CE	90	C. England	114
New Hall	G	11-18	RC	510	E. England	115
Oakham School	C	11-18	CE	950	C. England	116
Oxenfoord Castle	G	9-18	CE	100	Scotland	117
Polam Hall	G	5-18	ND	500	N. England	118
Rendcombe College	BC	11-18	ND	270	C. England	119
Rise Hall	G	11-18	CE	130	N. England	120
St. Augustine's College	B	8-18	RC	300	S. E. England	121
St. Christopher School	C	3-18	ND	460	E. England	122
St. George's School	{ BC / G	8-18	CE	300	E. England	123
St. John's College	G	8-18	CE	125	E. England	124
St. Joseph's School	B	7-16	ND	103	S. E. England	125
St. Leonards School	CG	3-16	ND	240	Scotland	126
St. Stephen's College	G	9-18	ND	450	S. E. England	127
Sevenoaks School	CG	4-18	CE	230	S. E. England	128
Temple Grove	C	11-18	Chr	900	S. E. England	129
Witham Hall	B	7-13	ND	120	C. England	130
Woodard Schools	C	8-13	CE	120	C. England	132
	B	11-18	CE	100	C. England	134
Wyvern House	{ B / G / M	13-18 / 11-18 / 4-18	CE / CE / ND	134 / 35	S. England	136

Specific details obtainable from the individual school in the group

Notes:

† i.e. preparation for the Common Entrance Examination.

* to be introduced shortly

Abbreviations:

B — boys only, BC — boys only except for mixed Sixth Form, G — girls only, CG — mixed pre-prep department, otherwise girls only, C — coeducational throughout, CE — Church of England, M — Methodist, RC — Roman Catholic, ND — Non-denominational, Chr — Christian, EFL — English as a Foreign Language, SCE — Scottish Certificate of Education (O Grades & Highers).

Please note also:

A small number of the schools represented here also

  i. prepare pupils of American Examinations and the International Baccalaureate

  ii. run summer schools for school children and/or adults which offer courses in English for Foreigners, sport, arts and crafts and various other cultural programmes.

Independent Boarding Schools

Note: Most of these schools also take day pupils.

Name of School	Type of school	Ages	Religion	Number of pupils	Common Entrance†	GCE O Level/SCE	GCE A Level	Oxbridge Entrance	Secretarial Courses	E.F.L.	Region	Page
Aldenham School	BC	13-18	CE	320	●	●	● *	●		●	C. England	94
Battisborough School	C	13-18	ND	65	●	●	●		●	●	S. W. England	95
Battle Abbey	G	10-18	CE	120		●	●	●	●	●	S. E. England	96
Bedford School	B	7-18	CE	1120	●	●	●	●		●	C. England	97
Beresford House	G	10-16	ND	200		●	●		●		S. England	98
Buckswood Grange	C	5-18	ND	65	●	●	●			●	S. E. England	99
Burgess Hill	G	8-18	ND	388		●	●	●			S. E. England	100
Caterham School	BC	11-18	CE	700	●	●	●	●			S. E. England	101
Croft House	G	3-11	ND	180		●	●		●		S. W. England	102
Dean Grange	C	13-18	ND	80		●	●			●	E. England	103
Dover College	C	7-18	M	360		●	●	●		●	S. E. England	104
Edgehill College	G	13-18	CE	425		●	●		●	●	S. W. England	105
Haileybury College	BC	7-18	ND	600	●	●	●	●			S. E. England	106
Holmewood House	B	7-14	CE	400		●			●	●	C. England	107
Howell's School	G	11-18	ND	350		●	●		●		Wales	108
Hurn Court	B	7-18	ND	150		●	●	●		●	S. England	109
Kent College	G	5-18	M	230	●	●	●	●	●	●	S. E. England	110
Kilgraston School	G	8-18	RC	210	●	●	● *	●	●	●	Scotland	111
Millfield School	C	13-19	ND	1150	●	●	●	●	●	●	S. W. England	112,3

93

ALDENHAM SCHOOL

H.M.C., Boys and Sixth Form Girls (Boarding & Day)

Founded in 1597 by Richard Platt, "Cytyzen and Brewer of London", Aldenham School stands in the beautiful rural setting of the gentle Hertfordshire countryside, some 22 kilometres from the centre of London, and only 40 minutes' drive from London Airport (Heathrow). It developed in the second half of the 19th century to become the small school (350 pupils) that we know today, with its tradition of boarding care, sound academic achievement and wide-ranging sporting success.

Most boys take the Common Entrance Examination at 13+, but the School makes special arrangements for interview and testing of those applicants who have not been prepared for that examination. All 13+ entrants take between 7 and 10 O-levels at 15+ and all pupils in the Sixth Form prepare 3 A-levels. More than half go on to universities and Further Education in the U.K. and abroad.

There are excellent facilities for Computing, Electronics, Languages, Art and Pottery and the School has a fine Library. Great emphasis is placed on the development within the individual of a well-disciplined approach to work and the fullest use of leisure-time. There is a wide range of sporting activities — from Soccer, Hockey and Cricket to Eton Fives, Tennis, Squash, Judo and Fencing, for example — and team sports and team spirit, as well as individual skill, are coached and encouraged by a dedicated and highly qualified staff. Music and Drama, also, have a strong tradition at Aldenham, and there are many clubs and societies, all of which give the individual the opportunity to develop his or her own talents and interests to the full. The proximity of London enables all pupils to benefit from the regular visits that are organised to the theatres, concert halls, opera, ballet, art galleries and museums of the capital. Senior boys and girls take responsibility for the day-to-day running of House and School.

Aldenham welcomes visitors to the School and to its extensive grounds, covering 135 acres.

Aldenham School, Elstree, Herts WD6 3AJ. Tel: Radlett 6131.

Headmaster: Michael Higginbottom, M.A., M.B.I.M., J.P.

BATTISBOROUGH SCHOOL

Battisborough was founded in 1955 by a master from Gordonstoun School, whose founder, the late Dr Kurt Hahn, was a governor of Battisborough for many years.

The school has a maximum of 65 boys and girls between the ages of 13 and 18 and aims to develop the strengths and potential of each student both as an individual and as a member of the community. All students live within the school campus.

All students are taught to GCE O Level in the usual range of subjects, but the organisation of the school permits some flexibility on the age at which the GCE is taken and allows for weaker candidates to take the CSE in addition. The American SAT and TOEFL exams and the Cambridge English exams may also be taken.

The size of the school, very small teaching groups, a weekly reporting system between the student's personal tutor, teachers and headmaster; the development of organised personal study habits combine to make Battisborough particularly suitable for those who dislike larger institutions or are transferring from another country's educational system.

In addition to some regular sporting activity during the week each student chooses a major weekend activity from canoeing, climbing, windsurfing and the expedition club and follows an appropriate programme which includes elements of other activities. As individuals become more proficient they are expected to assist in instructing others. This develops into a form of service, which with the Cliff Rescue, conservation and First Aid Work emphasises the individual's duty to be of help to others. Such use of the outdoors helps to instil self-discipline and personal motivation: qualities which further assist a student's academic progress and all-round education.

For families resident overseas, we are able to arrange end of term travelling; half-term programmes and an escort service from the London airports. Parents are always welcome at the school.

Battisborough School,
Holbeton,
Devon PL8 1JX.
Tel: Holbeton (075 530) 223.
Telex: 45639 Comput G.
Headmaster: Simon Gray, B.A., M.Phil.(Cantab).

BATTLE ABBEY SCHOOL

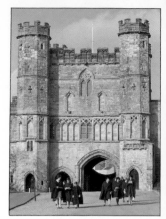

The Gateway.

An Independent Public School for Girls,
130 girls aged 10-18 including 30 day-girls.
Headmaster: D.J.A. Teall, B.Sc. (Newcastle).

Battle Abbey was founded by William the Conqueror to commemorate his victory in the Battle of Hastings on 14th October 1066. It became the home of the girls fo this famous Public School in 1922 when they moved from their former premises in Bexhill.

Situated in 52 acres of beautiful Sussex parkland. Battle Abbey School is proud of its reputation for providing a traditional English education of a very high standard within a caring family atmosphere. Here girls gain the necessary knowledge, qualifications, compassion and poise to enable them to make a positive contribution to society.

If you would like your daughter to become a Battle Abbey Girl, please contact the Headmaster's Secretary for further information or an appointment.

Battle Abbey School,
Battle,
East Sussex TN33 0AD.
Tel: 04246 2385.

BEDFORD SCHOOL

Bedford School is first mentioned in a document from the reign of Henry II. In 1566 it was endowed by Sir William Harpur, a citizen of Bedford, who became Lord Mayor of London. The present school buildings were opened in 1892 on what was then the edge of the town. On the night of March 3rd/4th 1979 the main school building was gutted by fire, but a new, modern school has been rebuilt inside the existing walls, combining improved facilities, with a redesigned Great Hall remaining at the heart of the building. Other buildings have been added over the years; these include the Chapel, the Memorial Building, Science block, Music School, Dining Halls and, more recently, a Recreation Centre containing a theatre, a swimming pool, squash courts and a sports hall.

The School is divided into three units, Preparatory School, Lower School and Upper School covering the ages 7-11, 11-13, and 13-18 respectively. Boys may join the School between 7 and 9, at 11, 13 or directly into the VIth Form. In the Preparatory and Lower Schools boys follow a wide general curriculum leading to Common Entrance or Public School Scholarship standard. In the Upper School all boys follow a broadly based course to Ordinary Level examinations taking between nine and twelve subjects.

The School has been involved for over a decade with courses in computing and all boys are given instruction in computer programming during their Mathematics lessons. The redevelopment of the Physics department will give additional scope for general courses in both practical computing and electronics. Computer courses are already available in the Sixth Forms, including one leading to A Level Computing Science.

In the Sixth Form most boys select three GCE Advanced Levels from a choice of about eighteen different subjects and boys are prepared for Higher Education courses. The most gifted are given special tuition leading to the Oxford and Cambridge Entrance examinations. All boys are encouraged to use 'out of school' time to develop their interests and talents in a large number of clubs and societies. Covering a wide field including sport, music, drama, community service, Combined Cadet Force, wood and metalwork, in addition to those societies such as the Pythagoreans or Electronics which give scope for specialist work in chosen academic areas.

Open Mornings are held in January but individual visitors will always receive a warm welcome. Further information can be obtained from:

The Registrar,
Bedford School
Burnaby Road,
Bedford MK40 2TU.

BERESFORD HOUSE SCHOOL

Beresford House School, which was founded in 1902, is an Independent Boarding and Day School for 200 girls between the ages of seven and eighteen years. It is a Charitable Educational Trust administered by a Board of Governors and is a member of the Governing Bodies of Girls' Public Schools Association.

The school moved to its present beautiful situation at the foot of the Downs in 1938, and acquired two adjacent houses to cope with its post-war expansion, and a separate modern classroom block was also added. Most recent additions include a large gymnasium/assembly hall, a third science laboratory and a well-equipped home economics and needlework block. There is also a good library which is well used by the girls.

The aim of the school is to give a liberal education on modern lines so that, within an academic framework, girls can develop their individual characters and talents, and acquire a social awareness in preparation for their life ahead. The school's religious and moral teaching is based on the Christian faith, but the school is open to girls of all denominations.

All girls are prepared for the General Certificate of Education at Ordinary and Advanced Level. In the junior school a sound general education is given by teachers well qualified to take this age group. This leads on to work in the senior school which is organised in four main subject departments: English, Mathematics, Science and Languages. To ensure an all-round education, all girls study English Language and Literature, History, Geography, Mathematics, Physics, Chemistry, Biology, French, German, Scripture, Needlework, Home Economics, Music, Art, Physical Education and Drama. Computer Studies and Latin are also available.

Girls in the Sixth Form prepare for the Advanced Level of the General Certificate of Education and for University, Polytechnic or College of Further Education entrance and the professions. Sixth formers can also take a secretarial course or additional 'O' Level GCE subjects, and a one-year General Course is available. The sixth form is regarded as a transition from school to college. The girls do not have to wear uniform, are encouraged to work on their own and to plan their own studies. There is a separate sixth form flat for the boarders.

The school is well-known locally for its high standard in choral singing as well as for its outstanding record in sport. All normal winter and summer sports are available and riding, sailing, golf and judo are offered as optional extras. The girls are encouraged to participate in the numerous School Societies and may also join the local branches of associations such as the East Sussex Classical Association and the British Association of Young Scientists.

The next School Open Day is being held on Saturday 7th July and a very warm welcome is extended to any interested visitor. Alternatively an appointment to see the school may be made through the School Secretary: Beresford House, Summerdown Road, Eastbourne, East Sussex BN20 8BS. Telephone 0323 31658.

BUCKSWOOD GRANGE

One of the few schools that, for many years, has offered overseas children full time English language programmes integrated into the curriculum and life of an English boarding school is Buckswood Grange, in Sussex.

Overseas boys and girls aged ten to sixteen are able to learn English in the School's own EFL (English as a Foreign Language) Department where small groups (usually less than eight) receive specialist tuition. These intensive English sessions are part of a specially designed curriculum including subjects such as art, music, computers, maths and games which accelerate the English language learning process.

Having achieved an acceptable standard of fluency in English, children are able to move on to the main boarding school curriculum where they are fully integrated with English children preparing for the GCE 'O' level. In this way, Buckswood Grange permits children to progress naturally with their education in the U.K. without a further change of school.

One reason for this School's success is its deliberately small size. The new student is easily assimilated into a well-ordered and friendly community; staff are able to give more personal attention to each individual; and small classes are guaranteed by the high staff ratio.

An additional feature of Buckswood Grange is its Summer School. This is held every year throughout July and August for boys and girls aged seven to sixteen. Its aim is to offer youngsters the opportunity to learn English and at the same time enjoy a memorable holiday. The activity rich programme includes sports — tennis, football, horse riding, swimming, etc. plus games and visits to the many places of interest in the South East of England.

Buckswood Grange, an elegant Regency house, stands in six acres of grounds — lawns and wooded areas — on the outskirts of Uckfield, a quiet Sussex town. It is particularly well located, being within easy reach of Heathrow and Gatwick airports, central London and the south coast sea resorts. The School offers a transfer service from and to the airports.

Those interested in visiting the School are always welcome; we simply ask visitors to phone a few days before so that we can make their visit as helpful as possible.

For further details please write, phone or telex for a School prospectus or Summer School brochure. The Principal, Buckswood Grange, Uckfield, East Sussex TN22 3PU. Telephone: Uckfield (0825) 3544 and 5010. Telex: 943763 Crocom G.

BURGESS HILL SCHOOL FOR GIRLS

The School occupies 12 acres of gardens, playing fields and tennis courts within easy walking distance of the railway station in Burgess Hill, which is a pleasant country town, in West Sussex, and on the main railway line to Gatwick and Victoria Station, London. The School buildings are developed from Victorian houses in a district of such architectural merit that, it has been designated a conservation area.

In 1981 a major building programme was completed. This included a large and well-equipped gymnasium and a unique octagonally shaped music school with individual and orchestral practice rooms.

There are approximately 330 day girls and 55 boarders. Day girls are accepted from 5 years and boarders from 9 years and there is a Nursery School.

A few places are available in our VIth Form of about 50 for girls from other schools.

The boarders live in three separate houses with young resident married staff. The emphasis is on creating a pleasant family atmosphere.

The excellent facilities include four Laboratories, an Art Complex and a Computer Studies Centre. Girls are prepared for GCE at 'O' and 'A' Levels in a wide range of subjects.

The School has its own entrance examination and there are several major and minor scholarships awarded each year. Visitors are always welcome and will be shown round the School. Please contact the Registrar or the Headmistress for an appointment or further information. We will be holding an Open Day on 7th May, starting at 2pm.

For further information please contact:

Burgess Hill School for Girls,
Keymer Road,
Burgess Hill,
West Sussex RH15 0AQ.
Telephone: (04446) 41050.

CATERHAM
SCHOOL

Situated in 80 acres of the North Downs, Caterham is within easy reach of Gatwick and Heathrow Airports and is less than 20 miles from London, by road and rail.

The Preparatory School of 250 boys aged 8-13, includes a Boarding house of 60, run by their Headmaster and his wife. Continuity is assured as boys move up from the Preparatory School to the Main School at 13. This consists of 440 pupils, with day girls in the Sixth Form of 170 and is divided into 3 Boarding and 4 Day houses.

The School provides a broad education based on Christian principles and practice. Pupils are prepared for the University of London O and A-levels, after which the majority go on to University or some form of further education.

Major games include rugby, hockey, athletics and cricket in the Main School and football, rugby and cricket in the Preparatory School. Optional sports are swimming (the School has a heated indoor pool), tennis, shooting, badminton, basketball and squash, with netball for girls.

Music is particularly strong with 2 orchestras, 2 choirs, a wind band, chamber ensembles. Debating and Dramatic Societies are also very popular and there is a Combined Cadet Force and the opportunity for Community Service.

Details of Assisted Places, Bursaries for sons of Servicemen, Scholarships (including Music) f r o m

The Headmaster,
Caterham School,
Harestone Valley,
Caterham,
Surrey CR3 6YA.

Founded in 1811
now celebrates its Centenary at Caterham.

CROFT HOUSE SCHOOL

History of the School

The School was founded in 1941 by Col. and Mrs. Torkington. By 1946 another property in the village was purchased.

General Information

The following subjects are available to 'O' and 'A' levels: — English Language, English Literature, Latin, French, German, Spanish, History, Divinity, Geography, Mathematics, Chemistry, Physics, Biology, Home Economics, Art History, Art, Needlework and Music. Needlework, Home Economics, Mathematics and French are also available as C.S.E. subjects.

When a girl reaches the upper third year she will be given a Tutor who will encourage and guide her in all aspects of school life. Two members of staff are actively involved in giving advice on career openings and there are talks every term by the County Careers Adviser. In the fifth form every girl is interviewed by the Director of the National Advisory Centre on Careers for Women.

Tuition can be provided on any musical instrument and there is a considerable amount of music making in the school.

Games include Tennis through the year, Netball, Hockey, Rounders, Athletics and Swimming. Judo, Yoga and Ballet instruction are available. Riding is an important feature throughout the school with its covered Riding School. The school is a recognised centre for the B.H.S.A.I. examinations and sixth form girls may combine this with other academic studies.

On four afternoons each week, girls in the fourth form and below have leisure activities of Floral Art, Orienteering, Photography, Pottery, Choir, Badminton, Craft or Olympic Gymnastics.

There is a flourishing Art Department and extensive studio facilities where girls are given a basic design course.

Weekend activities are arranged and include games, art club, walks, gymnastics, outings to places of interest, films, lectures, concerts and plays.

Much importance is attached to life in the sixth form where considerable responsibility is given to the girls in the day-to-day running of the school. This enables them to develop powers of leadership and prepares them for their future careers. Girls are directed to various forms of further education and training, ranging from Nursing and Secretarial Courses, to Colleges of Higher Education, Polytechnics and Universities.

Emphasis is placed on a full committment to all aspects of school life which will help to develop each girl's potential in the firm but friendly atmosphere of a Christian community. The school fosters excellence in all fields and gives encouragement to good manners, self-confidence and a love of learning.

The Croft House School,
Shillingstone,
Dorset.
Tel: Childe Okeford 860295.

DEAN GRANGE SCHOOL

Dean Grange School is situated in the most northerly village in Bedfordshire, on the borders of Cambridgeshire and Northamptonshire. Mentioned in the Domesday Book as Dene, meaning valley, many finds of pottery and bones suggest the possibilty of an earlier Saxon settlement. The church is a splendid survival from medieval times and amongst its interesting features are a canopied tomb with Lombardic lettering (1312) and a leper's squint. Other interesting buildings in the village include a lace school and the last remaining windmill in the north of the county.

When the village open field land was enclosed in 1800 two large properties with farms were developed. One by Mr Ackroyd, a Bradford businessman, which became Dean Grange and was known as the Manor House. The family lived in it until the Second World War when it was requisitioned by the Army for a Prisoner of War Camp. In 1946 the property was auctioned and purchased by a Miss Morley who, through some strange coincidence, was also Bradford born and bred. She and her partner moved from a small school in Harlow bringing with them six pupils and founded the present International School.

The wonderful future they forsaw for their project came to fruition and many hundreds of pupils of various nationalities were educated with loving care by the ladies and their staff. These pupils still return from various corners of the world with stories to relate and memories to talk over.

The present owners, Mr & Mrs Munday, also with connections in the North of England, have thoroughly modernised the ex-Manor House without losing any of its Georgian and early Victorian charm. The rural environment is appreciated by all who visit and the children certainly gain much from the happy atmosphere and freedom for play in the spacious garden and grounds, where chickens (domestic) and pheasants (wild) live side by side.

The staff all work together to create a warm, homely, welcoming atmosphere for the children, some of whom are not even English speaking. Sign language soon overcomes any barriers and the established pupils are only too willing to help all newcomers.

The educational standard of the children is above that which would be termed as 'average', the small classes and good facilities play a part in this, as does the atmosphere for work which permeates throughout the school.

For further information please contact:

Dean Grange International Preparatory School,
Dean Grange,
Upper Dean,
Huntingdon,
Cambs PE18 0LT.
Telephone: Riseley, Beds. (STD 023063) 243.

DOVER COLLEGE

The Chapel, Dover College 1906.

The College is set upon the historic site of the Priory of St Martin founded in 1139. The Priory was famous for its library and important as a hostel for travellers. King Stephen died within its walls in 1154; Parliament met here in 1263; and Chaucer and Erasmus were probably visitors. The Tudor composer Thomas Tallis was organ-master before Henry VIII dissolved the Priory in 1535. On the hill across the valley stands the great keep of Dover Castle, the key to England.

Dover College opened in 1871 to create a Public School in these attractive grounds. The monks' refectory is the dining hall; the guest house is the chapel; and the gatehouse is the headmaster's study. The College's charter was granted by King George V and Her Majesty the Queen Mother is our present patron.

Building on tradition the College is abreast of educational progress. It took the initiative and became fully co-educational in 1975. Recent developments include the creation of a computing centre, the opening of a new art department and the building of a large sports hall.

The College is proud of its open internationalist outlook and welcomes students from abroad, travel from the Continent being quick and easy. Our educational emphasis is upon variety of choice and upon the all-round intellectual, physical and spiritual development of each personality. Christian values are upheld and, while exam success is a high priority, academic training takes place within a larger context of culture, civilisation and caring.

The 360 students are accommodated in seven boarding houses. The teacher pupil ratio is low at 1:9; and in addition to his/her subject teachers and housestaff, each sixth-former has a tutor as a counsellor. Relationships between students and staff are exceptionally friendly and relaxed.

The College has its Junior School at Folkestone nearby, where brothers and sisters below 13 can attend.

A wide range of scholarships is offered to give recognition not only to academic talent but also to artistic and musical distinction. Details on request.

There is a College Open Day on 19th May; but at any time visitors are very welcome by prior arrangement. Why not break a journey from London to the Continent with a tour of the College?

Dover College,
Dover,
Kent CT17 9RX.
Tel: 0304 205969

EDGEHILL COLLEGE

Foundation: The College has a Methodist foundation and has always fostered Christian way of living.

Historical Development: We have always sustained a high standard of efficiency combined with moderate fees. Edgehill is an independent school which offers Assisted Places.

Philosophy of Education: We provide a happy friendly atmosphere and an exceptionally broad range of options for both Ordinary and Advanced Level. Our aim is to allow every girl to develop to her potential by finding her particular niche in life, so that she feels she can contribute something of value to the Community. To assist in this development we also offer a wide variety of leisure activities.

Curriculum: Pupils in the Senior School are prepared for G.C.E. at both Ordinary and Advanced Level. Music forms an important part of the School life and most girls learn to play an instrument. Examinations of the Royal Schools of Music are taken in a large number of instruments as well as Speech and Drama. There is a school orchestra, strings group and choir.

Games: We have an exceptionally fine games department: hockey, netball, cross country, gymnastics and volley ball are taught in the winter; tennis, rounders, athletics, and swimming in the summer. There is a badminton court in the gymnasium and girls are prepared for the Royal Life Saving examinations.

Facilities: The 50 acre estate comprises an unrivalled position in one of the most beautiful parts of North Devon. Situated on a hill on the outskirts of Bideford, it is within easy reach of the coast and the moors. The buildings are well equipped and constantly being improved and expanded.

Leisure Activities: We are ideally situated for Sailing, Canoeing and walking. Girls may participate in riding, trampolining, camping, modern dance, ballet, guiding, youth hostelling, fencing, orienteering, social service and the Duke of Edinburgh's award scheme.

Junior Department: This is a lively coeducational department where the children grow up in a happy and friendly family atmosphere with ample opportunity to develop both physically and mentally. Emphasis is placed on providing a thorough academic grounding balanced by a fund of creating interests.

Centenary: Our 1984 centenary appeal will enable us to add a splendid Sports Hall and hard playing area to our facilities.

Enquiries: should be made to:

> The Headmistress
> Edgehill College,
> Bideford,
> Devon EX39 3LY.

HAILEYBURY COLLEGE

Haileybury is an Independent Boarding School, or Public School, for boys from 13 to 18 years old (with girls in the two senior years) and a Lower School for 11 year old day boys. It stands in the Hertfordshire countryside 20 miles to the north of London. The fine classical facade is by William Wilkins, architect of the National Gallery in Trafalgar Square, and later architects include Sir Herbert Baker, who built much of New Delhi and many public buildings throughout Africa, including the remodelling of Groote Schuur for Cecil Rhodes. Haileybury's handsome buildings were designed first for the East India College, which was of University status, with many distinguished professors, including Malthus, the originator of the concept of population explosion.

The East India College closed in 1858 and Haileybury opened in 1862. This great school, which includes a Prime Minister among its former pupils, has always had an international outlook. Fifty three of this year's six hundred and ten pupils live overseas. The academic standing of the school is very high and a teacher pupil ratio of 1:11 ensures this. The subjects taught to University entrance level range from Greek and Latin to Advanced Mathematics and Combined Sciences, for which the school has very well equipped electronic and computer laboratories. Boys and girls are supervised individually by form masters and house masters, who monitor their academic progress and well-being from their point of arrival in the school until they need help or advice with choice of University or career. Extra curricular activities include twenty-two coached sports, excellent music, drama and art, and many clubs and societies catering for different interests.

The aim of the school is to provide a disciplined and caring environment from which to encourage each individual's personal growth in the pursuit of excellence.

Haileybury College,
Hertford,
Hertfordshire, SG13 7NU.
Tel: 0992 463353.

HOLMEWOOD HOUSE SCHOOL

The main building was designed and built in 1837, in beautiful grounds on the Kent/Sussex border, by the celebrated 19th Century architect Decimus Burton. Although the school was only founded in 1946, it soon became established as one of the country's leading preparatory schools, preparing boys for the top public schools. It became an Educational Trust in 1980, with a Governing Body which includes the Headmasters of three of the country's most famous public schools.

Now with its own Pre-Preparatory Department, the school educates 400 boys aged 4-13, 130 of them boarders. Situated within easy reach of Gatwick and Heathrow, all travel arrangements for the boys from overseas can be undertaken by the school.

The scholastic record is excellent, and Art, Music, Drama and Sport are of the highest standard. Computing is taught to all pupils.

With its many and varied activities the school aims to discover, develop and realise to the full the talents of its pupils in a caring community.

For further information and free prospectus, please write to or telephone the School Secretary, quoting HE, or make an appointment to view the school, when you will be made very welcome.

Holmewood House School,
Langton Green,
Tunbridge Wells.
Telephone Langton (0892 86) 2088.

Headmaster: D.G. Ives M.A.,
(Worcester College, Oxford).

HOWELL'S SCHOOL

Howell's School is a school of some 350 girls, primarily of age 11-18 but with a small and growing Preparatory Department of 50 girls, age: 7-10. The academic staff consists of 45 full-time and 14 part-time members.

The School has its origins in the year 1540 when a Welsh merchant, Thomas Howell, bequeathed the sum of 12,000 gold ducats in trust to the Drapers' Company, one of the ancient livery companies of The City of London. The present school was opened in 1859 and now looks back on a long tradition of excellence.

Howell's is a boarding school with a firm belief in the advantages which boarding has to offer. There is time in a seven day week to cover the academic curriculum in a broad and searching manner; there is time to pursue music and the arts and crafts; there is time to take advantage of the Snowdonian hills to the west, and the urban conurbations with their cultural amenities to the east.

There is also time to encourage a natural development of social skills. Each girl comes into contact with many others, with different interests and opinions. Learning to get on with others and learning to respect those who hold different views is very much a part of education.

The School has always had an excellent academic tradition. Scholarships to the value of over £100,000 are offered annually and the examination results consistently justify the faith of the School's benefactors.

Howell's is fortunate in both its magnificent physical setting and its facilities. The original school was purpose-built in a period when architects thought in generous proportions and more recent additions have continued this tradition. There are six science laboratories, a large library and a lecture hall equipped with video facilities. There is one of the finest sports halls in the country, playing fields of a standard high enough to have been used for international matches, a heated swimming pool, and twelve tennis courts. Currently under construction, and due for completion in late 1984, is an Art and Crafts complex of some 8,000 square feet.

The written word may be able to describe buildings but it can do little to convey the mood and enthusiasm of a school such as Howell's. A short video film is available on loan from the school (please specify format) but, should an opportunity arise, we would greatly welcome an opportunity of introducing you to the school in person.

Headmaster: J. T. Armstrong, M.A.(Ed), Ph.D.
Howell's School,
Denbigh,
Clwyd LL16 3EN.
Tel: (074571) 3631.

HURN COURT SCHOOL

Headmaster:
E.R. Morris, M.A.

Founded in 1952, Hurn Court School is mainly a boarding school for up to 150 boys, although day boys are sometimes considered. Pupils can join at 11-14. Those who come at 11 are boarded in a separate house a short distance from main school. There is no written entrance examination and entry is not precluded because of only modest academic ability. Indeed particular care and tuition is given to those who have learning difficulties.

Hurn Court stands in its own beautiful grounds of 30 acres on the outskirts of Bournemouth and Christchurch, bounded on all sides by farmland. It is easily accessible by either road or rail, with a fast motorway link with Heathrow Airport.

The buildings themselves date back to before the Reformation when the house was used as a Summer hunting lodge for the Priors of Christchurch. In the early 19th century, however, it was entirely rebuilt by the first Earl of Malmesbury, 'Le Lion Blanc', of diplomatic fame. The long, low farmhouse was converted into a stately mansion to which appropriate and well designed additions were made by succeeding Earls.

We maintain an excellent staff-pupil ratio resulting in very small classes. Boys are prepared for, and encouraged, to take GCE and/or CSE examinations in a wide range of subjects including English Language, English Literature, Mathematics, History, Geography, French, General Science, Biology, Physics, Art, Woodwork, Metalwork, Mechanical Drawing, Computer Science, Rural and Environmental Science.

Extensive metalwork and woodwork centres operate, and there is a flourishing school farm where pupils are encouraged to play an active and responsible part. An excellent computer centre has just been installed (September 1983). There are admirable facilities for games, drama, art and swimming. The school has its own ATC squadron, Sailing club and Modelling club.

The school is in the process of building a new Science block coupled with the addition of six extra classrooms. These should be in operation by early 1984 and will prove to be of great benefit in our constant endeavour to improve and expand the facilities available to our pupils.

Hurn Court enjoys space and beauty and a close family atmosphere. The premises are rich in history and in potential for forward-looking development. We believe that this happy combination can help to provide a sound foundation.

Prospectus and further particulars on application to:
The Bursar,
Hurn Court School,
Christchurch,
Dorset BH23 6AB.
Tel: Bournemouth (0202) 35812.

KENT
COLLEGE

The School was founded at Folkestone in 1885 and moved to Pembury in 1939, where it stands on high ground in 70 acres of woodland and playing fields in one of the most beautiful parts of Kent, and with easy access to Tunbridge Wells and Tonbridge and to London and the airports. Most of the school buildings, have been erected since 1950 and include a large Assembly hall gymnasium, a class room block extended in 1980, excellently equipped Science laboratories with a recent extension and residential houses including one with study bedrooms for VIth formers. The open air swimming pool is warmed by solar heating panels.

The girls follow an academic course leading to the General Certificate of Education at 'O' and 'A' level in a wide range of subjects, and go on to University and other places of further education. There are about 200 boarders and 160 day girls and these numbers include a strong VIth Form. Admission, based on the School Entrance Examination, is normally at 11 but can be in subsequent years including VIth Form.

There is also much emphasis on Music, Drama and Sport and on various leisure time pursuits in the boarding houses where a caring homelike atmosphere is fostered.

There is a separate Junior School, Aultmore, where pupils are received from Kindergarten to 11+. Here there is accommodation for 130, including 30 boarders (Telephone Tunbridge Wells 30715).

Prospectus and fees on application.

Headmaster: Rev J.C.A. Barrett, M.A.
Kent College,
Pembury,
Near Tunbridge Wells TN2 4AX.
Tel: Pembury 2006.

KILGRASTON SCHOOL

Kilgraston School is an interesting development. This broadly ecumenical school, housed in a red sandstone Adam mansion, sits solidly in the Perthshire hills. It is run by the internationally renowned Society of the Sacred Heart, and its strongly Church of Scotland-Episcopal-Catholic mix among staff and students makes for an unusually dynamic Christian community. Daughters of expatriates come from twenty-four countries for an education that is firmly rooted in tradition, Scottish and Sacre Coeur. Because of its tradition, the school can afford to be outward looking and is determinedly 'open'. The policy of care for the individual ensures that an exceptionally high percentage of its pupils go on to university via 'Highers' and 'A' levels. Its motto "Viriliter Age" has been re-translated "Act Purposefully" — a strong feminist note here!

Debating and public speaking are popular among senior girls, some of whom take part annually in national competitions. Friendly inter-school debates are stimulating and enjoyable social events. Girls are encouraged to develop wide interests, and the local hills are ideal for expeditions undertaken for the "Duke of Edinburgh Award Scheme".

Why not arrange visit to this beautiful part of Scotland to coincide with Open Day at Kilgraston, on Saturday, 16th June, 1984? Parents, friends, and 'Old Girls' enjoy a day with the school. There are exhibitions of work, displays of gymnastic prowess, a concert which includes speech and drama and choral works, and the needlework is displayed to advantage in a mannequin parade. You may join us for tea, or picnic in the beautiful grounds.

Kilgraston is set in 72 acres in the heart of Perthshire. Edinburgh, Blair Castle, and Glasgow are all within 45 minutes drive, and Perth, our nearest city, is a good base for visiting the highlands and the many historic and scenic places of interest in Scotland.

If you cannot manage to Open Day, you are welcome to visit at any time by appointment. Please contact us by telephoning 0738 812257, or by writing to the Headmistress.

Kilgraston School,
Convent of the Sacred Heart,
Bridge of Earn, Perth PH2 9BQ.
Tel. (0738) 812257

MILLFIELD
SCHOOL

Millfield (founded 1935) is an independent co-educational secondary school whose aim is to help pupils develop their individual potential to the full by achieving excellence in one or more of the many possible spheres.

Composition Wide range of academic ability. Academic and music scholarships awarded annually, as well as a large number of bursaries for all-round ability and potential. Extensive provision for treatment of dyslexia and English for foreigners.

Some 20% of pupils are foreign, from 30-50 different countries.

Situation Campus of over 40 acres in the heart of Somerset with surrounding boarding facilities and playing fields of 120 acres.

Size There are approximately 1150 pupils aged 13-19, 80% of whom are boarders. Teaching staff normally numbers 165. Most classes have about 10/11 pupils.

Curriculum Wide choice available from over 55 'O' level subjects with pass rate around 70% in recent years. Sixth Form of over 400. Normal 'A' level pass rate around 80% in nearly 40 subjects, with over 100 pupils each year gaining admission to universities, polytechnics and colleges in Britain or overseas. Several open awards at Oxford or Cambridge colleges each year. Teaching aids include closed-circuit television studio, large modern science laboraties, a large library and resources centre (of modern design) and two language laboratories.

Religion Multi-denominational, although with Christian bias: chaplaincy staff of six (two ordained and four laymen). Small chapel in regular use for Christian (including Orthodox), Jewish and Muslim worship, non-denominational meditation and private prayer.

Arts Instrumental tuition at all levels. Three orchestras, wind band, brass band, chorus, select choir and many instrumental groups. Formal and informal concerts. Theatre capable of seating 300: senior and junior plays and inter-house drama competitions.

Seven art and craft studios, including pottery, needlework, woodwork, metalwork and cookery.

Sport and Millfield Activities Programme Over 30 games played, many to international standard. Most team games take place at Kingweston, five miles away. Individual games based at Millfield, using sports hall, fencing salle, judo dojo, squash courts, swimming pool, health studio, riding school, rifle range, all-weather hockey pitch, 14 tennis courts and 7-hole golf course. Wide range of further hobbies, societies and outdoor activities covered by Millfield Activities Programme.

Millfield Junior School — Edgarley Hall, Glastonbury Separate notes are available. Aims and general philosophy almost identical to those of the Senior School. There are approximately 400 pupils aged 6-13 with small pupil-teacher ratio.

Applications Admission at almost any age is subject to satisfactory report and family interview. For further details, prospectus and application form write to Headmaster: Mr. C.R.M. Atkinson, B.A., M.Ed., D.L.C., Millfield School, Street, Somerset BA16 0YD. Tel: 0458-42291.

MILLFIELD SCHOOL VILLAGE OF EDUCATION

Activity Holiday Courses 1984
For individuals, families or groups.
23rd July — 17th August,
On the Campus of Millfield School in Somerset.

Aerobics, Amateur Dramatics, Anthropology, Antiques, Archery, Association Football, Art & Craft, Athletics, Badminton, Ballooning, Basketball, Birdwatching, Book Collecting, Bridge, Calligraphy, Canoeing, "Computer College", Cookery, Country Walks, Creative Writing, Cricket, Dance, Drama, Dressmaking & Soft Tailoring, Embroidery, **English for foreigners (Adults), English for foreigners (Children),** Fantasy & S.F. Games, Farmhouse & Cottage, Fencing, Fisher Technik, Fitness Training, Flower Arranging, French, Go-Karting, Golf, Guitar, Hovercraft, Jazz, Journalism, Judo, Linguistics, Metalwork, Model-Making, Multi-Activity Programme (5-13 years), Music Summer Schools, Nature Study, Oil Painting, Oriental Studies, Orienteering, Padder Tennis, Patchwork, Public Speaking, Photographic Workshop, Pottery, Riding (Pony Club C Standard), Riding For Recreation, Rounders, Rugby Football, Scottish Country Dancing, Shakespeare, Shooting, Sketch Club, Softball, Soft Toy Making, Squash, Swimming, Table Tennis, Tennis, Trampolining, Video-Filming, Village Cricket, Volleyball, Watercolour Painting, Woodwork, Yoga.

Take up a new sport or interest. Or learn more about your favourite one. There's a choice of 276 separate courses at Millfield.

Send or phone for a colour brochure: **John Davies,**

Village of Education,
Millfield School,
Street,
Somerset.
Tel: (0458) 42291.

NEVILL HOLT

Nevill Holt is a Manor House of varying periods ranging from c. 1400 to the 19th century. The Chapel dates from the late thirteenth century, its font from c. 1150. The central hall of the house is the oldest remaining room — some additions have been made, including an oriel window of c. 1465 and a fireplace of c. 1640 bearing the initials of Henry Nevill, a Colonel in the Royalist Army at Naseby.

The Nevill family, being Roman Catholic, found it difficult after the rise of Protestantism to distinguish themselves in political, judicial, or religious affiars. After the Civil War they suffered considerable financial penalties for having supported the losing side. By the 1860s they were no longer in a position to maintain the estate, considerably larger then than it is now. The Cunards bought Nevill Holt; the young Sir Bache followed current fashion and married an American wife famous in later years for her support of the cause of opera and Sir Thomas Beecham. The Cunards' only child Nancy was one of the Brightest of the Young Things of the Twenties.

The Preparatory School housed at Nevill Holt was originally founded in 1868 in Uppingham as a junior part of the famous Public School which celebrates its Quatercentenary in 1984. It was in 1920 that the Rev. C.A.C. Bowlker transferred the School to Nevill Holt which had stood empty since the departure of the Cunards. In 1928 it was bought by Mr. F.S. Phillips whose family own and run it still. Under them the School was developed and its facilities improved, so that it can now offer a wide range of sporting and cultural activities — drama, craft, music, rugby football, hockey, cricket, athletics, swimming, tennis, shooting and sailing.

The School prepares children (mainly boys) for all the famous Public Schools. Its philosophy is based on Christian teachings of morality and on concepts of courtesy, industry and self-discipline, so that every child may find some activity in which he or she can reach as high a standard of self-fulfilment as possible.

The Hall,
Nevill Holt,
Market Harborough,
Leicestershire LE16 8EG.
Tel: Medbourne Green 234.

NEW HALL SCHOOL

The history of the school now at New Hall, Boreham, in Chelmsford, Essex begins in the 17th Century when the first English Community of the Order of the Holy Sepulchre was founded at Liege on the 8th October 1642. This meant that the daughters of recusant families were able to receive the Catholic education denied to them in their own country during penal times.

In 1794 the school had to be transferred to England when its safety was threatened by the advancing French revolutionary armies. New Hall was finally selected as the most suitable site for the re-establishment of the school and, here, since 1799, in a house of great historic interest, it continues to the present day — enriched by the past, thoughtful for the future.

The years have seen progressive extensions and developments to meet current educational requirements. The school, now numbering 514 pupils, of whom 375 are boarders, has five middle school Houses, planned and attractively equipped for the 11-16 age range, each girl usually having her own cubicle. The separate Sixth Form "House", located in the main building and an adjoining new wing, accommodates a large group of students (to date 140) in an adult atmosphere suited to their age (16-18 years), interests and responsibilities.

The present curriculum is flexible and adapted to a wide range of ability. Centred initially on a common core of subjects — Religious Studies, English Language and Literature, Mathematics, one Science, one Modern Language — it includes further options such as Biology, Physics, Chemistry, History, Classics, Modern Languages, Computer Studies, Business Studies, Arts and Crafts, Music, Dancing, Drama, Home Economics.

There is ample provision for Physical Education in the two indoor gymasiums as well as in spacious playing fields and tennis courts, for athletics and cross-country events, for swimming in the heated pool, while a special feature of the school is its BHS (4 star) Riding School.

The normal age of entry is 11+, places being allotted on the results of the Common Entrance Examinations. A number of places are also available for VIth Form entries qualified for A Level work.

Every year on the 8th October our Foundation Day Celebration recalls the traditions, ideals and developments of time past — a cherished heritage, worthy of 'translation into modern life and thinking'.

New Hall School,
Boreham,
Chelmsford,
Essex CM3 3HT.
Tel: 0245 467588.

OAKHAM SCHOOL

Oakham School is a leading co-educational boarding school, situated at Oakham in the centre of England, surrounded by unspoilt countryside. The buildings of the School, some traditional, many modern and purpose built, and its fine playing fields, blend naturally with the town, and spread from the market square over 60 acres. It is within easy reach of London, East Anglia and the North of England. Founded in 1584 by Robert Johnson, Archdeacon of Leicester in a small building which is now a School theatre, Oakham today has 515 boys and 425 girls. Children may enter the School from the age of 10 years upwards.

Although Oakham is an academic school and has an excellent record in 'O' and 'A' level examinations and university entrance, it values the practical person as highly as the academic, the artist and musician as much as the sportsman. It is essentially a family school and the happiness of the individual boy or girl, at whatever level of achievement, is considered of vital importance to personal progress. From the 5th form onwards each pupil is assisted in planning for further education or a career, and parents are invited to take part. The School was one of the first to introduce computer education, and also has a business studies department.

All children are introduced to a wide range of creative activities. The Art and Design Centre offers courses in drawing, painting, pottery, sculpture, photography, woodwork, metalwork, jewellery, domestic science, screen printing and technical drawing. The School has a considerable reputation for its music and drama and the facilities are excellent; a new theatre will be opened during 1984.

Oakham is proud of the high standard achieved in many sports, but the priority is to introduce all pupils, whatever their aptitude, to a variety of sports and to stimulate enjoyment through skill.

The School is well endowed with scholarships and bursaries of which details are available on request to the Headmaster. The Headmaster welcomes visits from parents who wish to see what the School has to offer. Address:

Oakham School,
Oakham,
Rutland LE15 6DT.
Tel: (0572) 2487.

OXENFOORD CASTLE SCHOOL

Oxenfoord Castle, one of the ancestral homes of the Earl of Stair, lies twelve miles south of Edinburgh outside the village of Pathhead. The Castle, stables, Cranstoun Riddel and Cranstoun Church stand within beautiful and extensive grounds. The exact date of the oldest part of the house is not known, but James II is said to have stayed there. Considerable further extensions were made in 1840 by William Burn. Through the generosity of Lord Stair the house still contains a collection of valuable paintings, and the main rooms are furnished much as they were when it was a private house.

The School

Principal: Miss Mary Carmichael, B.Mus., A.R.C.M.

Oxenfoord is an independent boarding school for 100 girls, aged 10-18 years. The creative and performing arts particularly are encouraged. VIth form courses are Academic (in preparation for University entrance) and Vocational (cooking and homecraft). For information, details of entrance, scholarship and bursary examinations, and to see the School, please contact the Principal,

Oxenfoord Castle School,
Pathhead,
Midlothian EH37 5UD.
Tel: Ford (0875) 320241.

Music At Oxenfoord

The fourth Summer School of Music is from 25 August — 1 September 1984. The distinguished staff include Laura Sar Paul Hamburger and David Roblou. For information on the course please contact Joan Busby,

Easter Haining,
Ormiston,
East Lothian EH35 5NJ.
Tel: Pencaitland (0875) 340512.

POLAM HALL, DARLINGTON

Established in 1848.
An independent boarding and day school for girls.

The School stands in 23 acres of wooded grounds on the outskirts of the thriving market town of Darlington.

The original house was built in 1794, was considerably extended in 1825, and became the home for a small Friends School when the owners transferred their pupils from a Georgian town house into the more spacious accommodation and grounds of Polam Hall. The old hall is still the heart of Polam Hall today. The School, a limited Company under guarantee, came under the direction of a Board of Governors in 1939. It is now completely interdenominational.

During the last twenty years many developments have taken place and the school buildings much improved and extended. There are five well-equipped science laboratories; a new kitchen and spacious dining room have been added, a modern gymnasium and additional classrooms. Probably the greatest impact on school life has been made by the Liddiard Building with its foyer and theatre which is regularly used for professional and school concerts, as well as for our full-scale dramatic and operatic productions.

Every school is different, and Polam has its own distinctive features. Although quite close to the centre of Darlington, we enjoy beautiful grounds that are secluded and peaceful. Our buildings are diverse in style and interestingly assembled. All this enhances the quality of our life. Visitors notice also a relaxed atmosphere and a natural discipline. It is easy to be happy here.

Within our School, with all its natural advantages, our aim is to create lively and interesting people, who will have room to develop as individuals but will at the same time discover a capacity for living with others.

Our goals are many, and academically we aim high. We also strive to achieve excellence in other spheres: in music and drama, in our art department, and on the games field.

Visitors will find Darlington easily accessible, from Teesside Airport, the A1(M) and inter-city rail service from London.

For further information please contact:

The Headmistress,
Polam Hall,
Darlington,
Co. Durham DL1 5PA.
Tel: (0325) 463383.

RENDCOMB COLLEGE

If parents regard Independent Schools as offering an opportunity to exercise a discriminating choice, then Rendcomb must interest them.

Founded and generously endowed in 1920 by Noel Wills, Rendcomb had as its first Headmaster J.H. Simpson, author of "Sane Schooling", and took its place in the vanguard of post-war innovation. To the original eleven-year-old entry from Primary Schools there was soon added an entry at thirteen from Preparatory Schools, and in 1973 girls were taken into the Sixth Form. Thus the school has achieved a wide range of social background wholly in tune with the times.

Rendcomb is today a Headmasters' Conference School 260 strong. This size allows us to work as a single community in which each boy and girl may develop as an individual, while making an increasingly valuable contribution. Pupils are strongly encouraged to match their performance against their own potential and to avoid invalid comparisons with the attainments of others. There are no prizes, either for work or games, other than a personal sense of achievement. The standards reached under this principle speak for themselves.

The school has established a strong academic tradition. Most boys take ten subjects at 'O' level, and there are 44 combinations of 'A' level subjects available to sixth-formers, over 70 per cent of whom gain university places, including a number of places and awards at Oxford and Cambridge. The academic tradition is matched by a keen interest in sport, and a high standard is achieved despite the smallness of the school.

Its centre a nineteenth century mansion in the Italian style splendidly set in 200 acres of Cotswold parkland, the school has well equipped science laboratories and computer rooms, a language laboratory, library, reading room and an arts block for music, art, craft, woodwork and metalwork. All fifth-formers have studies and all sixth-formers have single study-bedrooms. There are seventeen acres of playing fields, a large sports hall, three grass and five hard tennis courts, two squash courts and a swimming pool.

We are always glad to receive visitors, and parties from overseas are especially welcome. We shall hold an Open Day on Saturday, 13 October 1984, from 10.00 am − 12.30 pm, when visitors are cordially invited to see the school at work.

For full prospectus or an appointment to look round, please ring:

The Secretary,
RENDCOMB COLLEGE,
CIRENCESTER,
GLOUCESTERSHIRE, GL7 7HA,
Tel: 028 583 213.

RISE HALL

Headmistress: Sister Geraldine Hall, C.S.A., M.A. Oxon

Rise Hall is a Catholic Independent Secondary Boarding and Day school for 140 girls, under the direction of the Canonesses of St. Augustine.

This religious Congregation was founded in Eastern France at the end of the sixteenth century and one of its earliest schools was at Compiègne. It was here that Queen Marie Lescynska, the wife of Louis XV, first met the nuns who were at that time living in great poverty, and she resolved to transfer them to Versailles. The convent she built for them was called the Couvent de la Reine and here the sisters taught girls of all social classes, with only those paying who were able to do so. It was from Versailles that the Canonesses came to Hull at the beginning of the twentieth century and to Rise after the Second World War.

The school is open to Christians of all denominations, with provision for Weekly Boarders and a separate Sixth Form House. It gives sound academic tuition from highly qualified staff and a full range of subjects to O and A Level and University Entrance, with special emphasis on the sciences, and three modern languages. It has an excellent games record and a good tradition in music, drama and art.

Rise Hall, a Georgian mansion in extensive grounds within easy reach of Hull, Beverley and Hornsea, offers a caring Christian environment, combining discipline with freedom and friendliness, and encouraging a sense of responsibility and intitiative.

Entrance Examinations are held each year in January and two Bursaries are available each year. For further information please contact:

The Headmistress,
Rise Hall,
Rise,
North Humberside HU11 5BL.
Tel: 0401 62276.

Parents are invited to attend our Garden Fête on 15th July, but are most welcome to view the school at any other time by appointment.

ST. AUGUSTINE'S COLLEGE

The Benedictine Order is rightly famous for its fifteen hundred years of educational and cultural tradition, not least in England which was evangelised by Benedictine monks. Since the Reformation, when all the great monasteries were destroyed, a dozen new English Abbeys have risen from the ruins. The first, historically, was dedicated to St. Augustine because it was built at Ramsgate within sight of the spot where the Apostle of England landed. Most English monasteries engage in educational work, though not all their schools are equally prestigious. St. Augustine's College, occupying fine cloistered buildings fifteen miles from Canterbury, is not one of the largest or best known, but has the unique distinction of combining more than sixty years tradition as a senior school with sixty more years of Preparatory School experience under the title of The Abbey School. Today both traditions flourish together on one site at Westgate in the Isle of Thanet.

St. Augustine's serves not only the locality of Thanet and Canterbury but more particularly the Catholic families who serve their country overseas and therefore need to find a boarding school at home for their children. It accommodates 200 boarders as well as 100 day boys, collaborating with the nearby Ursuline Convent School for girls, and prepares its pupils for the G.C.E. examinations that lead to entry to Universities at home and abroad. It is mainly the religious foundation and character of the school that draws Catholic children from the far corners of the earth, and here they learn to live and work and pray together in St. Benedict's "school of the Lord's service". Visitors are very welcome to St. Augustine's Abbey at Ramsgate, and to The Abbey School and St. Augustine's College, Canterbury Road, Westgate, Kent.

ST CHRISTOPHER SCHOOL

St Christopher School, Letchworth, Herts. (450 pupils, boarding and day) offers a complete scheme of education for boys and girls between 2½ and 19 years (boarders from age 7) with —

★ an emphasis on the needs of the individual child with education seen in a lifelong perspective

★ small classes, specialist staff and a wide range of courses in languages, arts, science and practical subjects

★ an excellent record of entry to universities (including regularly to Oxbridge) and to vocational training

★ exceptional facilities for drama, music and the creative arts (new theatre opened 1982)

★ a friendly informal caring atmosphere in co-educational boarding houses

★ vegetarian whole food diet and an emphasis on humane values and an international outlook

★ realistic involvement of pupils in school government, community service and challenging outdoor activities

★ an attractive campus on the edge of the First Garden City, one mile from the A1 and 38 mins from Kings Cross.

Admission may be considered at any stage up to the age of 13 and for direct entry to the expanding Sixth Form.

Prospectus from the Head:

Colin Reid, M.A.,
St Christopher School,
Letchworth,
Herts. SG6 3JZ.
Telephone: Letchworth (04626) 79301.

ST. GEORGES SCHOOL

St. Georges School is an Independent Boarding & Day School, fully registered with the Department of Education & Science.

The Boys Department (max 420 pupils) stands in parkland occupying 180 acres. Of this, 120 acres is taken up by an 18 hole Golf Course which is let to the Local Golf Club, although still available for School use. A further 30 acres consists of woodland available for pupils' recreational use — the remaining 30 acres being taken up by buildings and playing fields. There has been a Manor House on the site since 1254 when the first record of its existence was made. The existing Hall was built by the Pettiward family around 1794 and was designed by the architect Sandys. The Pettiwards continued in residence until the estate was broken up and sold in 1936.

St. Georges School Girls Department (max 200 pupils) stands in 6½ acres of Rural Norfolk and is housed in a grade 3 listed building. The School offers continuous education from 8 to 18 years and entry is possible at any age. All staff are fully qualified and mainly graduates: CSE/GCE O & A level course; maximum class size 20 pupils; traditional values, firm but reasonable discipline; good family atmosphere; sensible uniform — reasonably priced; extensive grounds — good sports facilities.

We will be holding an Open Day on 26th May, but visitors are welcome to view this School on any other occasion by appointment.

Boys dept: The Hall, Gt. Finborough, Stowmarket, Suffolk IP14 1EF.

Girls dept: Wicklewood, Wymondham, Norfolk NR18 9PR.

Headmaster: Mr. J.J.F. Robinson M.A. (Cantab).

ST. JOHN'S COLLEGE

St. John's College lies just outside Horsham, established in 1950. Since that date, many and varied alterations and additions have been made to help cope with today's demands and the inevitable increase in pupils. The classroom 'block' contains the normal Form Rooms and a Science Laboratory, a Geography Room, a Biology Laboratory, a Modern Languages Room, Art and Woodwork Centres. Adjacent there is also a Theatre cum Assembly Room, a Table-Tennis Room and a new Computer Centre is at present under construction.

A wide range of current technology and equipment encompasses all the demands expected of a modern school. The school is a centre for the Oxford G.C.E. Board. The timetable is so arranged as to ensure that pupils in the lower forms attend classes covering all subjects, academic and non-academic. In all forms, work is expected to take priority but no boy is expected to devote his entire time to academic tasks. The majority of team sports and individual pursuits are readily available, as are a wide range of activities and hobbies. An annual Ski-ing trip is much supported.

An active Careers Department, with frequent lectures, is available. The College's beautiful surroundings provide for a first-class Biology unit, making full use of the local environment.

At St. John's we like to think that a two-way system of discipline exists. Self discipline and that imposed by the school authorities. A generally contented atmosphere pervades the College. There is a constant flow of visits from 'old boys' and from parents of old boys. Social functions occur frequently through the year. Twice a term there are two nights set aside for Parent/Teacher evenings.

In school hours uniform is worn by all boys and defined casual wear is permitted at certain times.

We will be holding an Open day on 4th July, but visitors are welcome to view the school at any time by appointment. For further information please contact:

> The Secretary,
> St. John's College,
> Coolhurst,
> Horsham,
> West Sussex.

ST. JOSEPH'S SCHOOL, LINCOLN

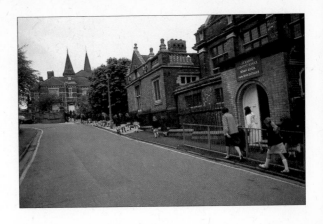

Boarding and Day School, girls 3-16, boys 3-8.
Denomination: Christian.
Date of Foundation: 1908.

Heritage: St. Joseph's was founded in 1908 by the Sisters of Providence who developed it from small beginnings until it occupied the campus site on both sides of Upper Lindum Street where it now stands. In 1983 the Sisters withdrew from the school and, rather than allow it to close, the parents set up a charitable trust which now owns and administers the school under the patronage of the Roman Catholic and Anglican bishops.

Location: Uphill Lincoln, in the shadow of the great cathedral, and near the remains of the ancient Roman City. In this historic and beautiful setting, girls receive a lively, modern education. The school buildings blend the old and the new as the school constantly develops courses and facilities to equip young women for their place in a challenging world.

Curriculum: English Language, English Literature, Spoken English, Drama, French, Latin, History, Geography, General Science, Physics, Chemistry, Biology, Human Biology, Mathematics, Music, Housecraft, Art & Craft, Needlework, Religious Studies, Gymastics, Netball, Rounders, Squash, Tennis, Badminton. Computer Studies are being developed.

Examinations: All girls sit for the London University GCE O level and East Midland CSE examinations in 8 to 10 subjects.

Extra Activities: Drama, Speech training, debating, ballet and modern dancing, swimming, sport, orchestra, choir. Instruments taught: violin, cello, clarinet, flute, recorders, guitar, piano. Others available on request.

Unique Features:
1. Continuity of education from nursery age to young adulthood.
2. Small classes where pupils' individual needs can be recognised and catered for.
3. It is the only girls' school in Lincoln and the only independent boarding school in the area taking secondary pupils.
4. It has both weekly and termly boarding facilities.
5. It is actively supported by the parents, whose loyalty and commitment have kept the school in being. St. Joseph's is known as "the school the parents could not let die".

For full details apply to:

The Headmistress,
St. Joseph's School,
Upper Lindum Street,
Lincoln LN2 5RW.
Tel: 0522 43764.

ST. LEONARDS SCHOOL

St. Leonards is an independent school for boarders and day girls. It was founded in 1877 with two main aims — to provide a school for girls where they would receive an education as good as that of their brothers, and to provide it in a setting where they would be taught by educated women.

St. Andrews, the seat of Scotland's oldest university, with its wide renown also as the home of Golf, provides an excellent setting for such a school. St. Leonards owns and occupies an historic site at the east corner of the town, close to the old harbour and the ruins of the cathedral. The thirty acres of parkland in which the school stands contain all the school houses, classrooms, laboratories gymnasium, playing fields and the medieval Queen Mary's house which accommodates the library.

At the time it was founded, St. Leonards represented ideas which were then wholly new in Girls' Schools but which soon came to be accepted practice. A high academic standard was set: girls successfully entered for public examinations and many went to the women's colleges at Oxford and Cambridge in the days when they first admitted women. In 1977 the school celebrated its centenary and was honoured by a visit from her majesty, Queen Elizabeth the Queen Mother who, as Duchess of York, had been the guest of honour at the School's Jubilee fifty years earlier.

St. Leonards is acknowledged to be one of the leading schools for girls in Britain. It has progressively adapted itself to changing circumstances and to fitting girls for lives and careers in the late twentieth century, while maintaining the standards of excellence set in the earlier days.

The school is governed by a council whose members are drawn from all parts of the country and represent the professions, academic life and business.

New projects completed in recent months have been the development of a computer studies department and new equipment is being added to this department in order to ensure that St. Leonards keeps thoroughly up-to-date with the latest developments in this field.

An old coach house was converted towards the end of 1982 and is proving extremely successful as a sixth form recreation area. Also in 1982, a language flexi-laboratory and drama room were established and swimming pool alterations were completed.

Plans are under consideration now for further developments to include squash courts, sports hall, music centre and house accommodation — all of which are envisaged as developments which keep St. Leonards in the forefront as a leading independent school in the United Kingdom.

The school offers several scholarships and bursaries to girls joining, attending and leaving the school and parents are invited to discuss all aspects of the school with the headmistress.

Visitors are warmly invited to visit the school on our Open Day, Saturday May 5th, or at any other time by appointement.

For further details please contact:

The Headmistress,
St. Leonards School, St. Andrews,
Fife, Scotland KY16 9LB.
Tel: 0334 72126.

ST. STEPHEN'S COLLEGE, BROADSTAIRS

St. Stephen's College is an independent girls' public school for both day and boarding pupils providing a sound education in an environment which is liberal yet well-ordered, offering support yet self-reliance.

The school was founded in 1867 by the Community of St. John Baptist, Clewer, Windsor, and moved to Broadstairs in 1946; new Sixth Form and dining accommodation was added in 1978. The Sisters of the Order ran the School until 1965, when they relinquished their responsibilities to a professional lay staff. St. Stephen's remains committed to traditional education in accordance with the faith and practice of the Church of England, but pupils of other faiths are welcomed. There are in all between 200 and 300 pupils, at least two-thirds of U.K. origin.

The Main School is for girls only, and offers a broad curriculum leading to 'O' and 'A' Levels in a wide range of subjects. Most Fifth Form girls achieve more than five 'O' Levels. A vital and dynamic Sixth Form sends a large proportion of its members to University and Training Colleges every year. A one-year Sixth Form course is also available, designed especially for European girls who wish to improve their fluency in English, combined with cultural studies and excursions. Computer Studies can be taken at 'O' Level in the Sixth Form.

The Preparatory Department is for day boys and girls aged four to eleven years, with Boarders accepted from the age of seven. High standards of education and behaviour are encouraged and there is a wide range of extra-mural activities.

Drama and music play a strong part in school life; in addition to the junior and senior choirs, there is a small group known as the St. Stephen's College Singers, which is frequently invited to give recitals in the area, and as far afield as London. Among varied leisure activities, including participation in local Leagues for a variety of sports, the School is one of only a few in the country to have its own British Horse Society Approved Riding School.

Four Main School Scholarships equivalent to one-third fees are awarded annually (two to eleven-year-olds, two to Sixth Form) and some Bursaries are available. A 10% reduction in fees is made for younger members of a family, and to families serving in H.M. Forces.

The College stands in a particularly attractive and healthy seaside location, with easy access to Channel Ports, as well as to London, Heathrow and Gatwick.

The College will be holding an Open Day on 17th May, but visitors are welcome at any time by appointment. Please Contact:

The Headmistress,
St. Stephen's College,
North Foreland,
Broadstairs,
Kent CT10 3NP.
Tel: (0843) 62254.

SEVENOAKS SCHOOL

Founded in 1418, today the school numbers 900 pupils of whom over 200 are boarders and over 400 in the Sixth Form, including 115 girls. From September 1984 the school will move towards full co-education at all levels. The buildings, on the fringe of Knole Park range in style from the 18th century Palladian to the uncompromisingly contemporary.

Like most good schools, Sevenoaks seeks to discover and foster individual abilities and talents as far as is possible within a responsible community, whose shared aims include academic success, physical health, moral stability and imaginative alertness. Yet every good school is unique in its emphases, in the balance it achieves between the competing goals of school life; the pleasures of self-expression and the rigours of intellectual discipline; a proper pride in oneself and a real concern for others; the healthy scepticism of young minds and their need to establish — or perhaps merely to glimpse — certain abiding moral values to help them confront, enjoy and contribute to a world now grappling confusedly with an era of rapid change. Parents and children considering Sevenoaks are urged to visit the school, preferably during the term, for in walking and talking and looking lies their best chance of imagining what it is like to be a boy or girl learning to grow up there.

The full range of normal school subjects is taught and there are excellent facilities for Drama, Music, Art and Sport. There is a new computer laboratory much used by the young, and computers play an important part in the teaching of science, geography, economics and mathematics. The Technical Activities Centre directed by Gerd Sommerhoff provides extensive facilities, including a wind tunnel, for any boy or girl with technical interests. The emphasis is on creative technology and on giving a free rein to the imagination — in keeping with the policy of providing many areas of activity in which pupils can develop their own ideas.

The school was a pioneer in the field of school-based community service. The Unit aims to give boys and girls an understanding of society by directly involving them — through practical jobs or shared activities — in the problems of the elderly, of young people in care or trouble, of the physically and mentally handicapped.

In 1962 a pioneering Sixth Form International Boarding House was opened, to enable bright British and overseas boys to live and learn together. In 1977 a similar house for girls confirmed our belief in the value of cultural interchange as did the establishment of regular term-time exchanges with French and German Schools. A further development has been the introduction of the International Baccalaureate as an alternative to A levels.

We will be holding an Open Day in November, but visitors are welcome to view the School at any time by appointment.

For further details please write to: Sevenoaks School, Sevenoaks, Kent TN13 1HU.

TEMPLE GROVE SCHOOL

Temple Grove is one of the oldest Preparatory Schools in the country, and traces its history back to 1810. For nearly a century it remained at East Sheen in Surrey, and in 1907 moved to Eastbourne. In 1935 the school came to its present site at Heron's Ghyll on the edge of Ashdown Forest and was formed into a Charitable Trust under the control of Board of Trustees in 1957. The Headmaster is a member of the Incorporated Association of Preparatory Schools through which he keeps in close touch with current educational thinking. A condition of membership of I.A.P.S. was formerly that the school must be recognised as efficient by the Department of Education and Science. Since April 1978, when the principle of recognition was discontinued, the I.A.P.S. has imposed its own stringent requirements for membership.

There is a full-time qualified staff giving a staff/pupil ration of 1 to 11 visiting staff for musical tuition. The majority live in the school grounds and thus help to foster the family atmosphere of the school. The youngest boys have their own form-mistress but, in the higher forms, staff specialise in their own subjects.

The 120 boys (aged 7½ to 13) are divided into nine forms numbering approximately 14 in each. All the main subjects are taught up to Common Entrance and Scholarship levels. There is a good record of Scholarship successes. Most boys still learn Latin, but a small group, unsuited to the subject for various reasons has separate classes during Latin lessons. Also included in the timetable are Art, Musical Appreciation, Physical Education and Current Affairs. A video cassette recorder is used as an aid to teaching when appropriate and a number of computers make a useful addition to the Maths Department facilities.

Alongside the academic curriculum there are considerable sporting amenities in 35 acres of parkland, with a gymnasium, all weather surface, spacious playing fields, tennis courts and a swimming pool. There are also a wide variety of activities which pupils are encouraged to pursue. These include Carpentry, Shooting, Fishing, Gardening, Archery, Judo, Fencing, Canoeing, Badminton, Basketball, Hockey, Modelmaking and a Model Railway Club.

There is a separate co-ed Pre-Preparatory Department catering for children aged between 4 and 7½. These pupils have the use of main school facilities.

For further information please contact:

The Headmaster,
Temple Grove,
Heron's Ghyll,
Nr. Uckfield,
East Sussex TN22 4DA.
Tel: (082 571) 2112.

WITHAM HALL SCHOOL

Witham Hall School (I.A.P.S.) is a small preparatory school of 100 (mostly boarders), which offers the facilities of much larger schools. There are hard tennis courts, a squash court, a music school, a computer centre, an audio-visual centre, artificial cricket wickets, a stage, and hobbies rooms, etc. Teaching groups are small and rarely exceed 12. The school has a fine scholarship and academic record, details of which are readily available. There is a full fixture list for major team games and parents are always welcome at matches. Individual games are also encouraged and coaching from a professional is available in squash and tennis. The school is fortunate enough to have close at hand a riding school and a water sports centre, where riding, water skiing, and wind-surfing are taught by experienced instructors.

Witham Hall is an attractive Queen Anne house standing in 15 acres of beautiful gardens and grounds in the village of Witham on the Hill which lies between STAMFORD and BOURNE. Parents looking for a small school which will aim to develop their children's talents and self-confidence in a caring environment are encouraged to visit the school in term time to meet members of staff and the children. The school offers a limited number of boarding places for girls (preference is given to sisters).

For an appointment and a prospectus please write to the Headmaster:

Peter Lyons, M.A. (Cantab),
Witham Hall,
Bourne,
Lincolnshire PE10 0JJ.
Telephone: Witham on the Hill (077 833) 222.

THE WOODARD SCHOOLS
IN THE MIDLANDS

Ellesmere College celebrates its centenary in 1984

One of the leaders of the great resurgence in education in Britain that took place from 1850 to 1890 was Canon Nathaniel Woodard. After founding Lancing, Hurstpierpoint and Ardingly Colleges in Sussex, Woodard turned his attention to the Midlands and before his death in 1891 Denstone, Ellesmere and Worksop Colleges for boys, and the two schools of S. Mary and S. Anne (later combined) at Abbots Bromley, for girls, were established. His aim was to provide a Christian boarding education for "children of the middle classes". Today the aim of a Christian education is maintained, although the schools of the Midland Division take day pupils as well as boarders and welcome a proportion of children of other faiths.

All the schools provide a broadly-based education combining the best of traditional syllabuses and modern developments. Healthy activities of all sorts are organised or encouraged and the building of character is given great importance. Facilities for recreational, cultural and sporting activities are excellent and all the schools are set in or close to beautiful open countryside. Most of the schools are housed in imposing buildings erected in the previous century, extended and adapted to modern standards. They are typical of the better medium-sized Public Schools and of the traditional Preparatory Schools which are the key elements in the British heritage of independent education. Those wishing to visit or learn more about them should contact:

The Divisional Bursar,
Wightman Chambers,
14a The Square,
Shrewsbury SY1 1LN.
Telephone Shrewsbury (0743) 56038.

Denstone College, Staffordshire. Boys and girls 13 to 18. Standing on a hill in fine countryside, the College has recently been in the news with an expedition to Inaccessible Island and involvement with the search for the Titanic.

Smallwood Manor, Uttoxeter, Staffordshire. Boys and girls 7 to 13. Preparatory school for Denstone College. The school occupies a country house in magnificent grounds.

Ellesmere College, Shropshire. Boys 13 to 18. Girls from 16 in VI Form. A major development programme has provided an Arts Centre, a Design & Technology Centre and VIth Form Study blocks for boys and girls respectively.

Worksop College, Nottinghamshire. Boys and girls 13 to 18. Set in 300 acres of grounds on the edge of Sherwood Forest. Recent building includes a theatre and a classroom block. High academic standards.

Ranby House, Retford, Nottinghamshire. Boys and girls 7 to 13. Preparatory school for Worksop College. Recently mounted a cycling expedition across the USA for charity.

Prestfelde, Shrewsbury. Boys 7 to 13. This preparatory school has an outstanding record of academic awards in recent years.

S. Hilary's, Alderley Edge, Cheshire. Day school for girls from 5 to 18. Lays strong emphasis on science subjects.

School of S. Mary & S. Anne, Abbots Bromley, Staffordshire. Girls 7 to 18. Set in a beautiful village, this famous school has a strong musical tradition and an excellent academic record.

Abbots Bromley has excellent sports facilities to complement its high academic and musical reputation

The Woodard Schools

FAITH

The first Woodard School was Lancing College, founded by Canon Nathaniel Woodard in 1848, and from this beginning has grown a Corporation of 25 Church of England Schools, with others which are associated. From the start the Schools were firmly based on the catholic faith as taught by the Church of England, and they still are. All the Schools are fee-paying and receive no central or local government grants. The maintenance of the Schools and their considerable development in recent years have been made possible by careful financial management and by the support of former pupils, parents and well-wishers. The Corporation's aim is to enable children from a wide range of backgrounds to benefit from a Woodard education.

Emphasis is placed on excellence and endeavour in academic work, leisure and sporting activities, and service to the community. In addition to achieving a high level of performance in public examinations, the Schools have gained notable success recently in music and the arts. Other developments include the introduction of computing and technical studies.

The community of the Schools is based on the importance of individuals, and the teaching of the Christian faith is fundamental to

AND SERVICE

their life and work. Through their chapels they aim to show that Christianity is a vital and realistic response to the problems of the twentieth century.

Details of entry requirements, etc. can be obtained direct from each school.

Ardingly College
Haywards Heath
West Sussex
RH17 6SQ

Bloxham School
Banbury
Oxon OX15 4PE

Lancing College
Lancing
West Sussex
BN15 0RW

Hurstpierpoint College
Hassocks
West Sussex
BN6 9JS

St. Michael's, Burton Park
Petworth
West Sussex
GU28 0LS

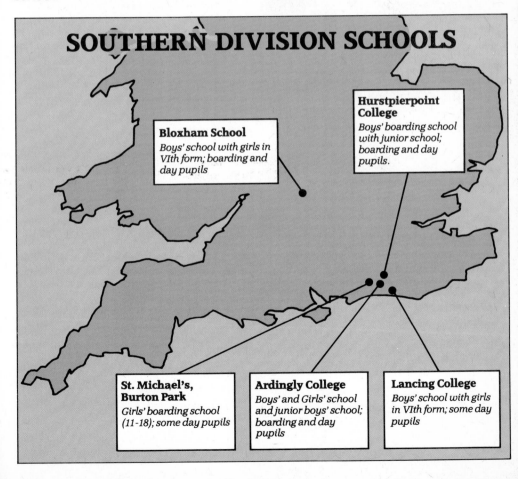

SOUTHERN DIVISION SCHOOLS

Bloxham School
Boys' school with girls in VIth form; boarding and day pupils

Hurstpierpoint College
Boys' boarding school with junior school; boarding and day pupils.

St. Michael's, Burton Park
Girls' boarding school (11-18); some day pupils

Ardingly College
Boys' and Girls' school and junior boys' school; boarding and day pupils

Lancing College
Boys' school with girls in VIth form; some day pupils

WYVERN HOUSE INTERNATIONAL STUDY CENTRE

The Director and Principal, Helen Tremain B.A., L.R.A.M., Cert.Ed. founded Wyvern House in 1977 because she wished to create a completely safe and happy family centre for the protection and education of students whose parents seek the best in English Education for their sons and daughters.

Helen Tremain lives on the premises together with her own family and all the girls are under her own personal care. The boys live in their own house on the same site and are under the personal care of resident houseparents. Full responsibility is assumed for the students night and day. Many of the students at Wyvern House are preparing for entry to an English boarding school or other schools where the medium of instruction is English.

Some of the students come for shorter, holiday courses and receive the same expert tuition as the full-time students, spending half the day following a course of English studies and the rest of the time on a programme of excursions and sports.

Course A. Preparation for Boarding School. Ages 9-16 years.
Course B. 'O' Level G.C.E 15 years and over.
Course C. Intensive English for Seniors 15-18 years.
Course D. Intensive English for Juniors 9-15 years.
Course E. Kindergarten 3-8 years.
Course F. Holiday Course All Ages.

The classes are very small and every student is treated on an individual basis.

Because Wyvern House is open every day of the year students can enter the centre at any time, if necessary at short notice.

Wyvern House is in the centre of Bournemouth which is situated on the south coast of England and is an important centre for language studies. Cinemas, theatres and concert halls provide a full cultural life. Beaches, sports centres swimming pools, golf courses and an ice rink are close by to be enjoyed by energetic students.

Visitors are welcome at any time by appointment. For further information please contact:

The Principal,
Wyvern House,
77 Lansdowne Road,
Bournemouth,
Dorset BH1 1RW.
Telephone (0202) 292608. Telex 418405 PDC G.

Reply coupons for further information

Please send them to the address of the institution in which you are interested

Heritage in Education

To *(name of institution)* ....

Please send me a copy of your current prospectus and application forms.

I am particularly interested in the following ....

....

....

Period of study to start *(date)* .... student's age ....

Name *(Mr, Mrs, Miss)* ....

Address ....

....

.... Country ....

I am a *student/*parent/ ....

I received my copy of Heritage in Education from ....

....

*I will be visiting your institution on the date given in your entry.

*I would like to visit your institution between ....

and .... Will you please arrange a suitable date.

(please delete as necessary)

Heritage in Education

To *(name of institution)* ....

Please send me a copy of your current prospectus and application forms.

I am particularly interested in the following ....

....

....

Period of study to start *(date)* .... student's age ....

Name *(Mr, Mrs, Miss)* ....

Address ....

....

.... Country ....

I am a *student/*parent/ ....

I received my copy of Heritage in Education from ....

....

*I will be visiting your institution on the date given in your entry.

*I would like to visit your institution between ....

and .... Will you please arrange a suitable date.

(please delete as necessary)

HERITAGE IN EDUCATION
INDEX

	Page
Aberystwyth, University College of Wales	7
Aldenham School	94
Anglo — World Education Ltd	34
Architectural Association, The	27
Basil Paterson College	62
Bath, University of	8
Battisborough School	95
Battle Abbey School	96
Bedford School	97
Beechlawn Tutorial College	63
Beresford House School	98
Blackburn Secretarial College	52
Bosworth Tutors	64
Brunel University	9
Buckswood Grange	99
Burgess Hill School for Girls	100
Cambridge Centre of Languages, The	35
Capital College	65
Caterham School	101
Chelsea College of Aeronautical and Automobile Engineering	28
Christ Church College, Canterbury	36
Clymping College	66
Connaught College	67
Coventry International English Studies Centre	37
Croft House School	102
Davies's College — Hove	68
Davies's College — London	69
Dean Grange School	103
Dover College	104
Durham, University of	10
Edgehill College	105
Edinburgh Language Foundation	38
Edinburgh Tutorial College	70
E.L.T. Banbury	39
Essex, University of	11
Greenwich Colleges, The	53
Greylands College	71
Hadleigh College	40
Haileybury College	106
Harrogate Tutorial College	72
Heriot-Watt University	12
Holmewood House	107
Houghton Education Centre	41
Howell's School	108
Hurn Court School	109
Imperial College of Science & Technology	13
International Language Centre	42
International Tutorial College	73
Irwin Academy	74
Keele, University of	14
Kent at Canterbury, University of	15
Kent College	110
Kilgraston School	111
Kings Schools Group, The	43
Lancaster, University of	16
Liverpool, University of	17
London Montessori Centre	29
London School of Insurance, The	54

Middlesex Polytechnic.. 25
Milestone Schools, The.. 75
Millfield School... 112/3
Mitchell & Deane.. 44
Nevill Holt... 114
New Hall School... 115
North Midlands Tutorial College....................................... 76
Oakham School.. 116
Oxenfoord Castle School... 117
Oxford Academy... 77
Padworth College.. 78
Pilgrims Language Courses... 45
Polam Hall... 118
Purley School of Languages.. 46
Regent School, The.. 47
Rendcomb College... 119
Rise Hall... 120
St Aldates College... 79
St Augustine's College, Westgate....................................... 121
St Christopher College, Letchworth.................................... 122
St George's School, Stowmarket.. 123
St Giles College... 80
St Godric's College.. 55
St John's College, Coolhurst... 124
St Joseph's Hall... 81
St Joseph's School, Lincoln.. 125
St Leonard's School, Fife.. 126
St Matthew's Tutorial College.. 82
St Stephen's College, Broadstairs...................................... 127
Salford, University of... 18
Schiller International University....................................... 24
SELS English College.. 48
Sevenoaks School.. 128
Southampton, University of.. 19
Stake Farm... 83
Stirling, University of.. 20
Strathclyde, University of... 21
Surrey, University of.. 22
Swan School of English, The... 49
Symondsbury College.. 84
Temple Grove... 129
Thames Polytechnic... 26
University Tutorial College.. 85
Warwick, University of.. 23
Wessex Tutors.. 86
West London College.. 56
Winchester Tutorial College... 87
Witham Hall... 130
Wolsey Hall.. 88
Woodward Schools, The... 132/4
Woodhill... 89
Wyvern House.. 136
                                                                    Page
Bolton Institute of Higher Education.................................. 30
Gabbitas-Thring.. 6,58,90
ISTA... 57
Schools Fees Insurance Agency... 131
Towry Law... 50
Youth Hostels Association... 131

Reply coupons for further information

Please send them to the address of the institution in which you are interested

Heritage in Education

To *(name of institution)* . . . .
Please send me a copy of your current prospectus and application forms.
I am particularly interested in the following . . . .

. . . .

Period of study to start *(date)* . . . . student's age . . . .
Name *(Mr, Mrs, Miss)* . . . .
Address . . . .

. . . .

. . . . Country . . . .
I am a *student/*parent/ . . . .
I received my copy of Heritage in Education from . . . .

. . . .

*I will be visiting your institution on the date given in your entry.
*I would like to visit your institution between . . . .
and . . . . Will you please arrange a suitable date.
(please delete as necessary)

Heritage in Education

To *(name of institution)* . . . .
Please send me a copy of your current prospectus and application forms.
I am particularly interested in the following . . . .

. . . .

Period of study to start *(date)* . . . . student's age . . . .
Name *(Mr, Mrs, Miss)* . . . .
Address . . . .

. . . .

. . . . Country . . . .
I am a *student/*parent/ . . . .
I received my copy of Heritage in Education from . . . .

. . . .

*I will be visiting your institution on the date given in your entry.
*I would like to visit your institution between . . . .
and . . . . Will you please arrange a suitable date.
(please delete as necessary)
